KENYA COLONY
D1234047
TANGANYIKA
by Paul White
NAIROBI
horn Trees
Mt. Kilimanjaro
Mt. Meru
ARUSHA
MOSHI
MOMBASA
Indian Ocean
BABATI
TANGA
KONDOA
ZANZIBAR
BUIGIRI
KONGWA
BEREGA
DAR-ES-SALAAM
MPWAPWA
MVUMI
Sisal
IRINGA
Rufiji River
YIKA
RITORY
East Africa
N
W
E
S

Melvin Sanoness
Christmas
1958

From
Mrs Melvin Anderson

Doctor of Tanganyika

DOCTOR OF TANGAN

by
Paul White

WM. B. EERDMANS PUBLISHING C

KA

RAND RAPIDS, MICHIGAN, 1957

First published in Australia, 1941
Published in revised and enlarged edition, in England, 1952
Published in American edition, 1955

LIBRARY OF CONGRESS No. 55-9739

This American Edition
published by special
arrangement with
The Paternoster Press, London

Set up and printed, May, 1955
Fourth printing, July, 1957

PRINTED IN THE UNITED STATES OF AMERICA

Dedicated

to my colleagues, African and European, in the
Church Missionary Society Hospitals
in Tanganyika Territory,
East Africa

Contents

Illustrations

DAILY LIFE

A DOCTOR AND HIS ASSISTANTS

AMONG THOSE WHO CAME

THE LITTLE ONES

AT MVUMI HOSPITAL

NURSES AND HELPERS

DEMONSTRATIONS, WARDS, CLINICS

MASAI PEOPLE

HIGH AWARD — AND FORWARD!

Doctor of Tanganyika

With thirty-four photographs by the author

CHAPTER 1

Tanganyika Hospital

"THAT'S enough anesthetic, Sister, thanks," I said, as I tied off a vein with a length of catgut.

I reached for a square of gauze, swabbed the wound, and proceeded to stitch it up with horsehair.

"Would you mind asking Daudi to focus the flashlight here again?"

The Sister murmured something in Chigogo, the local language. Immediately an African lad standing on a kerosene box shone a powerful beam on the little figure lying on the operating table. By its light I adjusted the dressings and fixed them in place with strips of adhesive tape.

I pulled off my surgical gloves and put my hands into lotion.

"What time is it, Sister?" I asked.

She peered at her watch in the miserable light of the hurricane lantern. Its smoky beam accentuated the weird shadows thrown on the tin roof by the rough-cut rafters.

From just outside the window came the sharp bark of a jackal. I started and upset some instruments. The Sister smiled.

"It's just midnight, Doctor."

For an hour and a half we had been operating, fighting for the life of a little lad who earlier that day had been impaled on a stake. In the gloom of a mud hut his parents had spent most of the day trying to push back protruding bowel, but without success. As a last resort the father had put the child on his back, and carried him seven miles to our hospital.

I bent over my little patient, and felt his fluttering pulse. I shook my head.

"I doubt whether he can stand it, Sister; he's terribly shocked."

"We can't even guess, Doctor, what they did to him at home, and then the witch doctor's efforts . . ." She shrugged her shoulders.

I gathered the little chap up in my arms and followed the Sister as she lighted the way from the improvised operating room to the mud-walled men's ward. Carefully I laid my burden on a rough native bed and wrote up his treatment in the ward book.

"I'll keep an eye on him now, Doctor. You go to bed; we'll call you if we want you."

I wiped the sweat from my forehead and somewhat unsteadily walked back through the starlight.

It was my third night in Africa. I was tired out but felt I just couldn't go to bed. I wanted to get my bearings. Before I left home I had known that I would meet this sort of thing, but here it was in cold, stark fact; primitive life, primitive conditions, unthinkable ignorance.

I sat down upon a crate to think. If I had not had those instruments and a sterilizer, I could not even have tried to do anything for that little laddie. Idly I turned over a sheaf of papers lying upon another packing case. On top was a letter I had received from the Sister while I was still in Sydney; one paragraph, underlined in red, caught my eye:

> Out here at Mvumi we are away in the African bush and have no electric light, no water piped in, or anything like that. Hurricane lanterns are our only means of lighting at the hospital; our water is carried in kerosene tins. It is heated on ordinary fuel stoves, and our only sterilizer is a fish kettle. The only instruments we have are a set of dilators, an antiquated pair of midwifery forceps, some scissors, a few artery forceps, needles (but no needle holder) and a full set of tooth extraction gadgets.

Daily Life

CHICKEN SELLERS

The birds are in the rope cage; their owner holds out his hand for the money, while the buyer turns disdainfully away.

"Timoteyo . . . was an adept at disguising the inevitable chicken, which he bought with sugar or safety pins, for the equivalent of threepence each. Eggs were another main item of food and for these the cook would make his assistant bring a bowl of water so that every egg could be carefully tested. Those which floated to the top were indignantly rejected." (Everyday Doings)

GOGO
LIFE

"In front of flat-roofed squat houses, with gardens of sorghum and maize, women sat pounding and grinding." *(Kongwa–Berega)*

GOGO HOUSES
NEAR KONGWA,
NORTHEAST OF
MVUMI

A Wakaguru family and their round, conical-roofed hut.

IN BEREGA,
EAST OF
KONGWA

I remembered how I had prayed for the instruments and how my prayers had been answered. I looked over the typed list of the contents of the eighteen crates piled in my room:

(a) Eye instruments — purchase price, three pounds, ten shillings.

(b) Obstetrical and general surgical instruments — purchase price, five pounds.

I remembered the first item. An auction sale had yielded one hundred and thirty pounds worth of instruments for two guineas, and then the second lot, worth nearly five hundred pounds, had come my way for five pounds. My eye ran down the list; sterilizers, syringes, hypodermic needles. I knelt beside a box and thanked God for supplying all these things, and asked for His help in the job that lay ahead.

The African night was full of strange noises. A hyena howled dismally near at hand, and from the distance came sounds of a native dance. I listened to it all, so new and strange to me, and as I blew out the lamp my thoughts were fixed on the size of the task I had undertaken. Then I remembered God's solemn promise to me, and its conditions. Those words that had meant so much to me as a schoolboy, an under-graduate, and in my hospital days:

> Trust in the Lord with all your heart and do not lean on your own understanding. In all your ways acknowledge Him and He will direct your path.

In those crates there was evidence in the form of instruments, drugs and dressings; tangible evidence of the way God had kept His side of the contract.

My first day had been spent going around the hospital, where I was shown the various buildings in the order of their construction.

Here was the mud-brick ward where the maternity work had started; there was the hole from which the cobra had emerged in the middle of the arrival of twins.

Over there was the men's ward. By the light of the small windows I dimly saw the six beds in the mud-and-wattle building. Turning, I collided with a pole that held up part of the mud roof, and, in the gloom, nearly fell over an ingenious locker that had been contrived from an old gasoline case. The only luxury in that primitive ward was the concrete floor.

As I came out again, the strong sunlight dazzled my eyes. Next I was taken to a little room that had once been a kitchen, but had now been turned into an emergency operating room. The mud of the roof had been covered here and there with sheets of *bati* (a much simpler word for the natives than corrugated iron), held in place by great lumps of granite.

Next we visited the building where outpatients are seen, and I was shown where prenatal patients slept on a built-in veranda. Then we came to the new wards — fine stone and concrete buildings, each housing twenty beds, well lighted and ventilated, and admirably fitted up to suit local conditions. The whole place was crammed with people, all clamoring to be examined by the new doctor.

First I ran the gauntlet of outpatients and shook hands with all and sundry, greeting each with:

"*Zo wugono?* — How did you sleep?"

All were most impressed that I should have such a grip of their language, and said:

"*Kumbe! Ya namya* — Behold, he knows!"

They were to be disillusioned at noon, when a new set of greetings came on — I was not up to more than two new phrases in one day!

Placing my brand new helmet carefully out of range of the *dudus,* or insects, I sat down to the biggest outpatient job of my limited career. There were a hundred and twenty women and children, all ages, sizes, and degrees. Some were neatly dressed, some in utter rags, but all anxious to see me, and my methods. There was a subdued hum of interest as my stethoscope appeared, and a positive buzz of enthusiasm when I produced a battery-lighted gadget for examining ears.

Of course, everything had to be carried on by interpretation. Africans delight in describing vividly and in minute detail each and every irrelevant symptom, and, whenever possible, illustrate generously with pantomime.

There were skin diseases by the score, deep, stinking ulcers, heavily infected scabies, angry thorn wounds; lepers, infectious and non-infectious. There was one girl with a disfiguring scar, impossible to remove except with radium, of which there was none in the Territory. There were paralyzed children, and eye cases of all kinds. I saw mere babies with scarred, sightless eyes, the result of a witch doctor's treatment; others had eyes matted with pus and swarming with flies. Old folk with cataracts were led in by their relatives. Malaria cases, huddled up in blankets, sat shivering in the hot sun. Then came a series of minor ailments; coughs, colds, burns, cuts and bruises, and lastly, those who would like to taste my medicine.

By lunch time I felt completely overwhelmed. I had seen enough major surgery to keep me going all day, every day, for a week, quite apart from the host of diseases that this country especially favors.

In the afternoon the staff turned out in force to help unpack. I had my first lesson in Gogo exclamations that day as instruments came to light:

"*Kah!*" said Daudi, as the lid came off a crate and the sterilizer was disclosed..

"*Kumbe!*" gasped Samson, on seeing the surgical instruments, while Sechelela, the old African matron, produced a classic, "*Yaya gwe!* — Oh my mother!" as she saw our green glare-reducing surgery linen.

The dressers bore off the steam sterilizer in triumph; the collapsible operating table went to the hospital on a nurse's head; I shuddered to see a jar of catgut following in a similar style. However, everything arrived safely and was put in the temporary operating room.

But my surgical introduction to Africa was to be a tragic one. Two days after my first operation, very unwillingly, I attempted to remove a tumor from a little girl's back. She was little more than a baby and the tumor was the size of her head. Her eight-year-old sister brought her to us, carrying her pick-a-back. I made a diagnosis and decided to operate. To my deep concern it proved to be an extensive cancer. An X-ray would have made everything clear, but as such diagnostic luxuries were not available, I had the frightful experience of seeing the child die from shock in the operating room.

Two hours later I was called to the men's ward to see the boy who had been impaled on the stake. He had obviously taken a turn for the worse, and, though I did everything possible and remained with him the whole afternoon, he died at sundown.

In my first week at the hospital, two surgical cases had died.

That night I could not sleep. The thump-thump of drums and the wierd chant of the dancers, the howling of jackals, and donkeys braying, all produced a strange uncanny atmosphere. I got up from my bed and walked up and down the room, going over each case a hundred times. Had it been my fault? Could I have done anything more?

I stood watching the moon behind the gnarled limbs of baobab trees. My only conclusion was that the odds were heavily biased against the surgeon here. Cases came in after shocking interference, often in the last stages and suffering from a variety of tropical diseases, to which was added that accursed legacy of so-called civilization, venereal disease.

CHAPTER 2

Everyday Doings

"HOME!" said my wife. "It looks rather queer, but it's the first that's ever been really ours."

We stood outside the squat, whitewashed building with its irregular tin roof and mosquito-wire-covered windows. I took her arm, and we stood watching the African carpenter putting back part of the door frame. He had had to remove one side of this, so that our second-hand piano could be carried in. Elisha hammered in a final nail, and we walked over the threshold of our Tanganyikan home.

Philip and Nathanael, our houseboys, dressed in spotless white *kanzus*, carried in a cot, in which slumbered our ten-months' old son. We stood looking down at him. I smiled.

My wife drew me into the building.

"Come and look at everything. Let's see the furniture, and measure the windows for curtains."

We were in the dining-room. The table had crude bush timber legs. I looked at these, and up at the door posts. Mary followed my glance, and smiled.

"Anyhow, the door frame matches the table legs!"

There was another piece of furniture, of doubtful classification, which already was holding our chest of tableware. Two bent-wood chairs and a curtain rod suspended on two rusty nails completed the furnishing. Through an irregular doorway was a completely empty room, with a view of blue hills through its glassless windows. Off this was the bathroom. We walked across the uneven floor of pounded lime and sand, and looked in. I was not reassured. Two kerosene tins covered with a bath-mat, and a slightly lop-sided galvanized iron tub in which we could bathe by the instalment plan, was all that was available. But in the corner was a box, nailed down. I had paid a pound for the contents of that crate.

A huge Belgian in Dar-es-Salaam had helped me to turn a watering can, a four-gallon bucket and a two-way tap, into a most respectable desert shower bath.

The bedroom door was stuck. I pulled vigorously, and a shower of white-ant-eaten board fell as it opened. The room itself faced north, and had a wide outlook of cornfields, plain, and hills. A torn canvas blind flapped dolefully against the mosquito wire.

"That wire doesn't look very lion-proof," remarked my wife. "But I'll have to put up with that, I suppose, since I *would* marry a missionary who is an obstetrician."

I had reason to remember that remark when some time later I had gone up to the hospital for a midnight emergency operation and had seen several hyenas skulking round the back door. I knew I was leaving my wife alone with young David, with nothing but an inaccurate .22 rifle in the house by way of protection.

The bedroom certainly was furnished. There were two beds; one, the work of a native carpenter, was mattressed with criss-crossed rope; the other, a patriarch among iron bedsteads, had bulbous brass knobs and a mattress that had been extensively repaired with binding wire. However, there was a real chest of drawers and an ungainly wardrobe.

Little had been said during this tour of inspection but, at the end of it, we looked at each other and laughed.

"We're missionaries, now," said my wife. "I'll do what I can to brighten up this place. Some pictures and a few odds and ends of cretonne will give it a very different appearance."

I nodded. Words are not a very suitable vehicle to express what you feel when your wife can smile at tremendous difficulties and set to work to build up a home from the crudest of material!

A window covered with spider-webs opened into an unceilinged storeroom, which we christened "the ballroom." I dealt with an oversize black spider, and we peered into the room. Dimly I could see the outline of piles of crates, and over by the window was Elisha, carefully removing nails from the lids.

By elaborate signs and a mixture of Swahili and English, I managed to make him understand what I wanted made from those empty crates. The piano case was to become a dresser, and the lid of it the essential portion of the dining-room table. Packing cases would become chests of drawers, wardrobes, armchairs, and the baby's play pen.

Elisha wrote these instructions laboriously on the back of a piece of three-ply, and limped off to his workshop.

A few weeks later, with a pint of permanganate solution and some white ant killer to camouflage the bareness of the planed boxwood, we had our "Jungle House" adequately furnished, at a cost of thirty shillings!

Some native mats, costing a few cents, did something to soften the hardness of the irregular floors, and remnants of cretonne and some bright watercolors arranged by a woman's artistic touch produced a most attractive home.

One evening, during my first month in Mvumi, I sat drinking coffee that had been grown near the shores of Lake Victoria Nyanza. The wind blew noisily through the baobab trees, a loose piece of corrugated iron rattled intermittently, and in the native village donkeys brayed and drums throbbed. It was all very strange to me, but to the veteran Church Missionary Society pioneer, Archdeacon Briggs, who had spent forty-seven years in Ugogo, they were everyday sounds.

He was sharing our evening meal. Putting down his cup and turning to me, he said:

"Your house has gone through a few adventures since it was built in 1903. Originally, it was one of the first schools in Tanganyika. Later, we built a better school, and turned the old place into a rest house for missionaries on safari.

In 1914, the Germans used it when they came over here and took me prisoner, and since then parts of the roof have been blown off twice by hurricanes."

Then he told me of the days when he first came out and walked up from the coast, camping in the jungle among hostile people, and in waterless desert. I heard of serious illness with no doctor available, of teeth extracted by the patient himself, of adventures with animals, insects, floods and famines. I looked with a new understanding at this intrepid pioneer, and felt that our new home really had all modern Tanganyikan conveniences.

I fell into a reverie, and thought of the Archdeacon's doings from a variety of angles. Chicken — tough and tasteless, costing threepence, and worth about half that sum — had been the main meat portion of his diet for nearly half a century. His carving of the scraggy birds was a pleasure to watch. Ponderously I worked it out in my head: 2 x 50 x 365.

"About thirty-six thousand dead chickens," I murmured aloud.

"Pardon?" said the pioneer.

I looked up guiltily. "Sorry, sir. I was just working out how many chickens you must have carved since you arrived in Tanganyika!"

The old man laughed, and then told me something of the guile of the early chiefs, and finished up by comparing them with the present Mutemi of Ugogo, Mazengo. It was his father, Charlula, who so irritated Stanley.

Mazengo is one of the mainstays of our work; he and his family patronize the hospital regularly. Several of his children have been born there, and his influence and enthusiasm were one of the main factors in the building of our base hospital and the extensive Girl's Boarding School at Mvumi.

Soon after my arrival, the chief and his retinue came to greet me. I said all the Gogo greetings I knew, and listened to a translated speech of welcome. He then took me to see some places of outstanding interest at Mvumi. He showed me the track that Alexander Mackay had followed, and the baobab near which he had camped. Then we went to the hospital, and, standing between two wards, he said:

"It was here, Bwana, that my grandfather defeated the Wahehe. The main battle was fought on this hill. The enemy was driven back across the Ruaha River, fifty miles south. Now you have come here, and your hospital is built on the place where we fought for our freedom. My grandfather won that battle, and you have come now to fight a new battle against sickness and death, and to help us to be a stronger and a better tribe. You are only a young man, but since you are married and have a child, you are very acceptable to the Wagogo."

Then he went to greet my wife. The chief put out his arms to my small son. David immediately went to him, and to the huge delight of the crowd and of the great man himself, pulled his nose!

I have always been struck with the way in which the Africans can handle a child. They have the knack of picking up and comforting a child, and, no matter how fearsome their aspect, never seem to inspire fear in children.

One day David, who at that time could walk only shakily and talk very little, met me as I was on my way to the hospital. He was hand in hand with as fierce looking a specimen as you could ask to see. This warrior carried in one hand a six foot spear, sharp as a razor, of the kind described in the tourist book as "a triumph of native craftmanship," but which, if examined closely, would almost certainly be inscribed: "Made in Birmingham." As he caught sight of me, David left his new friend and came toddling towards me, and said:

"*Ayu muswanu* — He is a good man."

The big Mogogo smiled with delight, and said:

"*Kumbe! Ayu yali Mugogo mweneco* — Behold, he is a real Mugogo."

It would be useless to seek a chief cook in Ugogo. In no time you have a staff of at least five, all of whom are firmly convinced that they are part and parcel of the establishment. They speak of "our forks," "our spade," or "our children." It is a case of one man, one job — and those jobs are in watertight compartments.

The houseboy, who does washing, ironing, and general cleaning, would feel it a tremendous indignity to be asked to water the garden; while once I caused a great outcry by making a request to the cook boy that he should iron some shorts for me. "He would burn them, Bwana, or crease them down the sides!" cried the outraged *dhobi,* as the offending garments were snatched away.

When the rainwater is used up, our water supply comes from a well in the garden a mile away. Mhutila, who carries it in two kerosene tins on a pole, makes ten journeys a day, as well as pottering about our flower garden and pulling out our choicest seedlings. When the moon is suitable, he starts his work at 5 a.m., and, oblivious of hyenas, has all the water drawn by 9 a.m. As he nears the house he whistles and sings in the way peculiar to water carriers at the end of their journey. It may be melodious, but I could not appreciate it fully in those small hours before dawn.

My first experience with cooks was rather unfortunate. Justino was lazy and unpunctual, and produced burnt chicken, unbaked potatoes, and no matter what sweet was ordered, he produced some modification of rice pudding. One day I returned to lunch and found a curry so hot that it was quite inedible. I called for the cook, who came in sheepishly. In very broken Chigogo, I gave him a good lecture, and then told him to sit down in a corner and eat the whole dishful of curry. After a mouthful, tears began to stream down his face, tears purely produced by the curry. For a few more weeks we endured his cooking, but it was impossible, and he had to be dismissed.

"You will give me a letter, Bwana, so that I may get other work?"

"I will give you a letter all right!" I said, and wrote out the following epistle for him:

> "The bearer, Justino, has in three months never been on time or shown any signs of efficiency.
>
> "Regarding his cooking, I can only say that he is an excellent footballer."

A fortnight later I received a misspelled but radiant letter from Justino, telling me that he was now cook to an Indian, and that my letter had been the cause of his getting the job. Later, I learned that this Indian spoke not one word of English!

Timothy, who was the next to hold this office, was given the help of a diminutive assistant who cut wood, broke dishes, and was supposed to clean the pots. Timoteyo, as he was called in the local tongue, was made responsible for the cooking. He baked excellent bread, and was adept at disguising the inevitable chicken, which he bought with sugar or safety pins, for the equivalent of threepence each. Eggs were another main item of food and for these we paid a shilling for fifty. When buying these the cook would make his assistant bring a bowl of water so that every egg could be carefully tested. Those which floated to the top were indignantly rejected.

Most of our everyday needs are bought at the back door. All manner of people bring their goods to sell. The *Washenzishenzi* — or "utter heathen" from miles around bring eggs, fowls, limes, and fat-tailed sheep, together with native stools, baskets, and all manner of handicraft. Almost always we can get pawpaws and green vegetables from Matthew, a teacher, who steadfastly refuses to be paid for his evangelistic work, preferring to sell his fruit and vegetables for his living. We supply his seeds, and in due course buy the results. He carries his goods in baskets on a pole, but if he cannot manage to make the six-mile journey himself, he sends his wife with a loaded basket on her head.

Our own garden by the river is an oasis. There are great shady mango trees planted by the pioneers, banana and pawpaw trees, and spinach and spinach and spinach!

The gardener's name is Esau, a friendly soul who took a great interest in my language problems. On one occasion I told him to put the bugs in bags so that the birds could not get at them. Old Esau very kindly and solemnly corrected me:

"*Si gali makuguni, Bwana, gali mankogoni* — Not bugs, sir, they are grapes."

Each evening at sunset two figures came over the hill, past the church, to our kitchen door — a man and his wife, who were our firewood merchants. In true Gogo style, the husband walked ahead of his wife, with his load on his shoulders. The woman followed with a bigger bundle carried on her head.

If he has two good meals a day, and his cows are well, the average Mugogo is content. When the rains come, he cultivates; when the crop is in ear, he scares away birds and monkeys. Every year, before the rains, he builds or repairs his flat-roofed house. The rest of his time he looks after his cattle, finding pastures for them, sometimes having to travel fifty miles to do so. Then, again, he will spend hours doing nothing at all, just strolling round the countryside, or playing *wusolo* — a native game which is a cross between checkers and the broad jump — at a tremendous rate.

They are slow to change their ways, slow to adopt new methods, but, whatever their faults, their keen sense of humor makes them a most likable people.

Whenever you walk around the village everyone has a greeting for you, and everyone seems glad to see you. A stool is at once brought out, and you sit down to chat, while the women pound and grind within the house in preparation for the evening meal. They are very simple folk. They ask about the children, and are very concerned to hear of any sickness. You inquire after their children, and all come to say "*Mbukwa* — Good-day." Even the baby, dressed solely in a string of beads, is brought out to see you, and the toddler, with bells on his ankles to encourage him to walk, comes over to pull your finger or play with your watch. You are shown the new calves, and discuss the dowry price of the eldest daughter.

Girls are not sold here for so many cattle, but a dowry is paid over to the girl's relatives by the husband's people. These cattle are collected after great discussion between all branches of the family, and are distributed amongst various members of the girl's clan. Should the marriage threaten to "die," there is a fine to-do. All the girl's relatives meet and discuss and argue, and in this manner minor differences are often settled amicably.

In Ugogo, for a woman to be childless is a tremendous stigma. She is scorned by her fellow villagers, and spends her substance on the barbaric treatment of the old hags who "specialize" in "*Wutamwa we wacekulu-cekulu,*" or "women's special complaints." The marriage almost always "dies," the cows have to be returned, and the girl goes back in shame to her father's house, while the husband finds himself another wife.

Again and again these cases have been brought to me, and, with the aid of a small operation or a series of injections, these unfortunate women have been able to have an infant. One such home, where there had been repeated wife beatings and intense misery, became the absolute reverse when the long-desired baby at last arrived. Incidentally, I received great *kudos* from this particular case, since every "practitioner" in the district had been beaten by it and had declared that nothing could be done.

Arriving home one evening at sundown, I was just about to put on my mosquito boots when I saw the postman, Hezekiah, with the mailbag slung over his shoulder, coming up the hill. His biweekly safaris are our only postal service. He walks twenty miles over native paths and through animal-infested forests to reach us.

There are few disappointments more real than a mailbag producing nothing but the weekly *Tanganyika Standard* and a collection of medical circulars asking intimate questions about your liver and your various bodily functions. On the other hand, what a grand feeling it is to see letter after letter from home and a bundle of months-old newspapers. You read the papers from end to end, even classified advertisements, and "Personal and Missing Friends."

CHAPTER 3

Mpwapwa and the Governor

A PICTURESQUE messenger in a red fez that looked like a flower pot upside down, came to the door with a letter in a cleft stick. He had walked twenty miles through the thornbush and lion country that separated our Jungle Hospital from the railway town of Dodoma. I tore open the envelope, and read:

> Dear Doctor,
>
> The christening has been fixed for Sunday at three. Will you be godfather?

I wrote an answer, and, as I was putting it into the envelope, I turned round to the hospital Sister:

"I'm going to be a godfather. It seems all very nice, but it will be great fun getting in over the black soil. I'll probably have to walk."

"Why don't you go to Mpwapwa while you're about it?" she replied. "There's an all-weather road from the railway station and we've had a week's dry spell. You've got a grand chance, and you could catch Thursday's freight train."

"But how about the hospital here, Sister?"

"Oh, there is only Luka, and his wound is draining nicely. Take this chance and see the clinic down there."

My job was not only to run the Base Hospital, but also to supervise six others, distributed all over Tanganyika. Up to that time I had not visited any of these, so it was arranged for me to go the next day on the freight train, and I sent a wire back by the messenger to the hospital at Mpwapwa, telling them to expect me.

There had been no rain for some days, and the chances of getting through to the station seemed excellent, but that night it poured. At 3 a.m. I struggled out of bed sleepily, lit a hurricane lantern, and gathered up a collection of dishes, basins and pots. There were six main leaks in our house, and each had a receptacle, according to its capacity! I satisfied myself that everything was in place, and then shone my flashlight through the mosquito wire and saw our hard won garden swamped by a brown torrent. Swirling, blinding rain made it impossible to see five yards ahead. It *would* have to rain like this when I had arranged to go on safari in the morning!

I went back to bed to listen to the drip, drip of the rain in the big dish that reposed in our best armchair. After twenty minutes it was all over, and the roar of the rivers became audible as they rushed down from the hills. My last waking thoughts were of those first miles on the way to the main railway line, with their five rivers and a morass of black mud to cross.

At dawn, my gardener arrived and said the road was so bad you could hardly walk. The cook shook his head and said:

"*Nzila mba muno muno* — It is a very rotten road."

But the mailman had heard from a district foreman, a huge fellow with an ornate vocabulary, that he intended making the trip to Dodoma that day, so off went an envoy, to catch him at his camp on the far side of the local bog, to beg a lift.

I hunted out my football boots, put on my worst shorts and shirt, and, with a lad to carry the baggage, ploughed my way over those three miles of squelchy, slimy, sticky black mud, and seated myself on a can of gasoline in the back of a "Bedford" that had covered a hundred thousand miles, and looked like it.

We were most of the day traveling thirty miles. The safari was a long succession of getting bogged and getting out again by the aid of monster jacks and great chocks of

A Doctor and His Assistants

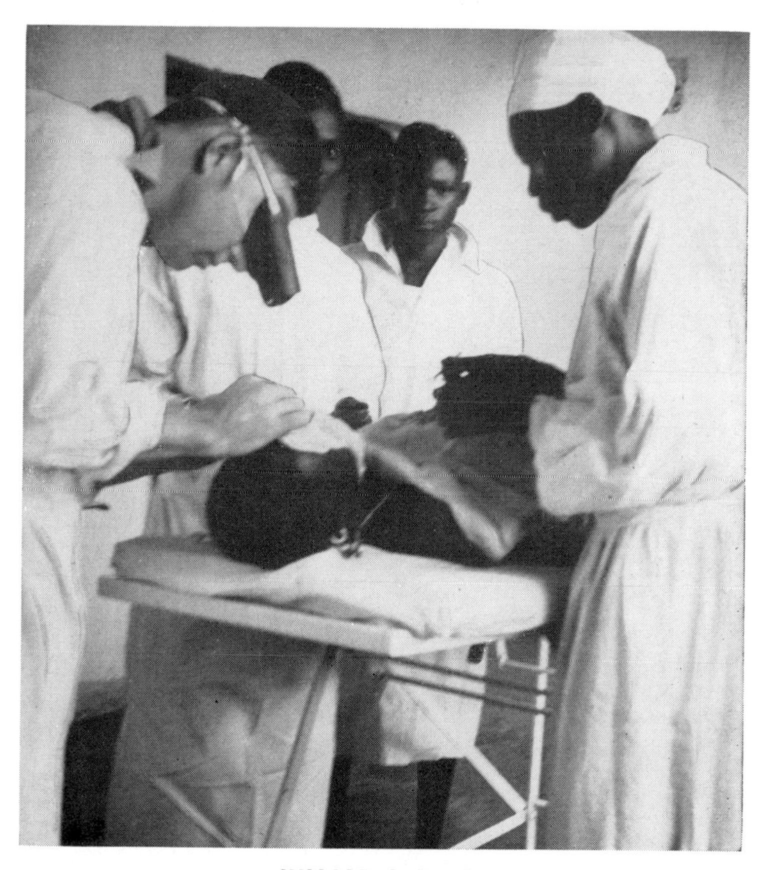

JUNGLE SURGERY

Cataract Operation in progress; Daudi assisting the author

"The first Monday afternoon of the month was specially set aside, obstetrics permitting, for making up my monthly report. . . . Two thousand four hundred and sixty-two outpatients seen; thirty cataracts done; twenty-eight of them had gone home under their own steam, full of the praises of the hospital. They could see again after years of blindness." (At the Hospital)

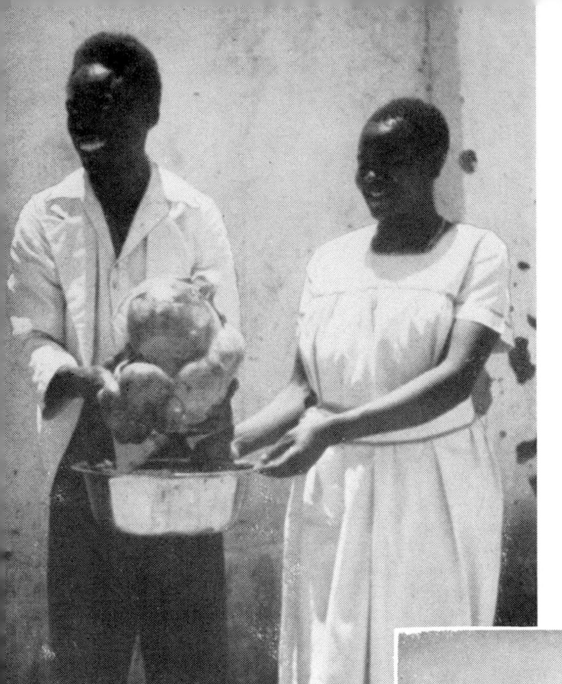

TRAINED AFRICAN PATHOLOGIST

"He is a sample of young educated Africa." (Staff)

DAUDI AND HIS WIFE MWENDWA

— *"Are we not a hospital family?"* — and the tumor that weighed fifteen pounds.

(We Build, Under Difficulties)

PASTOR MIKA AND CHIEF MAZENGO, KING OF UGOGO

(German Days and Gala Days)

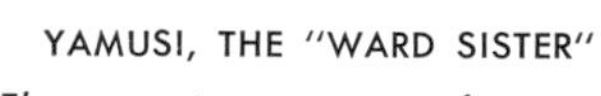

YAMUSI, THE "WARD SISTER"

"The very strong prayer of a man who is right with God is most effective." (Fleas and Fungus)

timber. Ultimately, at sunset, we reached Dodoma, looking indescribable and feeling utterly weary.

After tea and a bath, I set out for the station, hunted up the assistant station master, and purchased a second class ticket on the freight train to Gulwe. He looked rather queerly at me, and then said:

"But where is your chair?"

"Chair?" I queried, and discovered — after various by-laws had been read and a flowery oration made by the Indian officer — that on a freight train one supplied one's own seating and lighting, if such luxuries were required. I had neither chair nor lantern.

Then I could not find the train.

"It is down there, Bwana," said an African, pointing with his lips in a direction roughly east.

In the darkness, I stumbled over rails and steel ties (which resist white ants, but are a tremendous temptation for the native blacksmith), and at last got into a luggage car without springs, and made myself comfortable on a bag of potatoes.

Presently, in walked a big, cheerful Yorkshireman. He grasped my hand and told me he was going east to Morogoro, half a day's journey as trains go in Tanganyika, to bring up the Governor's train. With a crash and a bump, we were off, the red embers from the engine glowing behind us as we moved slowly round a curve and on through the darkness.

My companion told me a number of yarns of his experiences up and down the line. At one place his engine had hit a giraffe and they had been held up for two hours in consequence. At another, the railway had been moved several miles south, as the original German roadbed lay twenty feet beneath the surface of a lake that had appeared after a particularly heavy rainy season. He told me, too, of a narrow escape when a tropical downpour had washed out the road.

It was most stimulating to sit there, and, as the train rattled on through the blackness of a Central African night, to listen to this engine driver's first-hand experience of God.

"It was back in Yorkshire, Doc," he said, in a voice that reminded me irresistibly of Stanley Holloway imploring Sam to "pick oop tha moosket," "it was back in Yorkshire that I asked Jesus to be my Savior, and to be at the controls of my life. And, believe me, He's helped me to keep on the rails, and to go ahead."

My companion had proved the value of prayer, and illustrated his points by parallels from his job. His was that simple, sincere faith that is most convincing, and it seemed a very natural thing, as the train neared Gulwe, for us to kneel together beside that bag of potatoes, and to commend ourselves and our work into the Almighty's care.

It was midnight when we arrived, and intensely dark. An Indian in overcoat and muffler came up to me and said:

"The Doctor, is it?"

I nodded, and he took me over to his truck. We drove off up a steep hill, winding ever higher through thick forest. Three large civet cats, black and white striped, with immense, bushy tails, ran in the light of the headlights; a hyena bumped our front fender; then, entering a long avenue, planted in the days of the German occupation, we ran into a veritable colony of owls.

In the starlight of the early morning, I had my first view of Mpwapwa. Three generations ago Stanley had passed through this town on his historic search for Livingstone. I could well appreciate his feelings, as I stood on the side of the steep, jungle-covered hill and looked out over the moon-lit plains. Far out to the east was a great silvery lake, and range upon range of mountains radiated out from the town over Ugogo.

What had impressed Stanley most about Mpwapwa was its insect population! He was frightened that his tent would be eaten by the white ants while he slept. He found the earwigs most trying, and they still swarm all over the place. I was reminded of this by the sleepy houseboy who showed me my room. His parting instructions were:

"Look between the sheets before you get in, Bwana. You never quite know what might be there!"

I was awakened at daybreak by the chatter of women coming to the hospital. After breakfast there were a hundred of them crowded round the little grass-thatched building. My knowledge of the language was as yet very small indeed, so I sat down, with some misgiving, to deal with the crowd. Mwendwa, the midwife, came and tried to explain something to me, but I could make neither head nor tail of it. At last she grasped my hand and led me to the door. To my great relief, I realized that most of the women had come to welcome me, and not for treatment.

First I looked round the hospital. The place was run by African nurses, who had only a monthly visit from an Australian Sister, whose hospital was twenty miles away over the hills. Everything was neat and clean.

In the general ward were five beds of native make. Rough-cut bush timber comprised the frames, the "wire" mattresses were, as usual, made from baobab bark rope. Kapok mattresses are unheard of, but a palm-leaf mat (costing four pence) served to keep the ropes from leaving a pattern on the patient. Two cotton blankets, at six shillings a pair, and cheap, unbleached calico sheets, costing half that price, made up the bedding.

In the corner was a kerosene tin of drinking water, carefully covered with a bit of mosquito net, and above it a variety of medicine glasses. It had been found that the top of a tomato sauce bottle held exactly a tablespoonful. The African nurses were very intrigued at this discovery, because it was almost impossible to break these improvised measures.

In another corner was an ingenious native broom, while on the top of a cupboard was the inevitable insecticide gun, used both to deal with mosquitoes and wasps, and to spray the relatives of patients, who, we felt, would probably add to the flora and fauna of the ward unless we took this precaution. It is a solemn ritual that each visitor must be sprayed before he or she may enter the ward.

In the maternity ward were colorful charts, showing how to bathe baby, and how to feed, to wean and to train him. Instruments were carefully put in a gasoline case cupboard, and dressings were stored in kerosene tins, skilfully cut down, and painted white.

I could find no fault with old Mwendwa's work. It was a very real testimony to the care and thoroughness with which she had been trained, and showed how well these African folk can do when they are given a responsible task.

I looked at the babies, little chubby, dusky-pink people. My knowledge of the language was extremely meager. However, appreciative noises and a smile conveyed to the delighted mothers what I thought of their offspring.

Then I went and sat at my packing-case desk under the grass roof of the veranda, and, armed with my stethoscope, prepared to see all who had come for medicine.

For fully half an hour I employed my small vocabulary to very good effect, and gravely shook hands with everybody. Then, for three hours, by dumb show and gesticulation, I treated dozens of women and children.

It was amazing how effectively you could deal with, and cure, many tropical diseases by simple, inexpensive means. I was struck by the fact that a few pennyworth of eye drops were sufficient to treat fifty patients that morning.

I shall never be able to forget one incident that occurred. A little lad was brought in with two staring, sightless eyes. He was covered with skin disease, but the thing that horrified me most was the condition of his toes. Nearly a century ago, in the days of the slave trade, a tiny insect, the ground flea, had been brought across in slave ships from South America. It had traveled over the thousands of miles from the West Coast, and had found its way almost universally into the dust around native villages. It affects people by burrowing under the skin of the toes, and there it lays its eggs, producing a very irritable swelling beneath the skin, about the size of a grain of wheat. Almost every

African carries in his pierced ear lobe a more or less rusty safety pin, which he uses for taking out the insect and its egg sac. In any village you may see an African dexterously digging out the *funza,* as they call it in Swahili, from his friend's toe, with the previously mentioned weapon.

Unfortunately, the little blind lad had no one to help him in his difficulties, and his toes had literally been eaten away by this parasitic flea. I couldn't speak to him. My knowledge of the language was too small. But in him I saw the tragedy of African childhood — blinded by the witch doctor, neglected by his parents, and suffering helplessly from the perpetual itch of skin disease, and from the nagging ache of his insect-riddled toes.

The tiny hospital is characteristic of how much can be done with very little. It consisted of a mud-walled, grass-thatched building with six native beds, which cost fifty pounds to build, and which is given an upkeep allowance of twenty-five pounds a year, a staff of three African nurses, an odd job man and a water-carrier donkey. With this as a working basis, three hundred babies were born in the hospital in a year. In addition, welfare talks were given and personal contacts made by the senior African nurse, who tramped miles over the mountains, visiting villages in the forest and greatly helping both mothers and children, building up confidence in the hospital and helping us, by dealing with diseases in the early stages, to save lives. In this way that practical Gospel, which is the heart of the teaching of Jesus, was preached.

That evening I sat hunched up under a mosquito net and wrote my report. I summarized it "A grand little clinic, doing extensive work at bare minimum cost."

Mpwapwa is a beautiful spot. Built on green slopes and overlooked by steep granite-topped crags, ablaze with red acacia, it looks over range upon range of blue mountains and the silver waters of Lake Kimogayi.

I stood above the little hospital and looked towards the village over the grass roof of the maternity ward. Down the hill from the hospital was the road to the native town.

Women walked up from the wells with tins and calabashes on their heads, their babies peering wide-eyed over their shoulders. Near the river were enormous umbrella-like thorn trees, shading the fifty-yard-wide stretch of dry sand, which, after a thunderstorm, was a raging torrent. The town had the usual collection of mud brick and corrugated iron shops. Hurricane lanterns, chunks of brown sugar, kerosene, and famous brands of biscuits, all stood side by side in the heterogeneous conglomeration of the dusty little *dukas*. On the other side of the river is the Government Pathological Laboratory. The doctor in charge was always most helpful. As a matter of fact, he put the finishing touches on the training of a number of our African boys, who became extremely skilled in the use of the microscope.

My arrival in Mpwapwa coincided with the official visit of the acting Governor. The town was in top form. Flags were out, as also were strangely misspelled notices of welcome. But the crowning feature of the day was a huge calico sign, with letters alternatively red and blue, reading:

"GOD SAVE THE KING FROM THE
INDIAN COMMUNITY"

Very greatly against my will, I had forced upon me a cup of weak tea in a cracked, and far from cleanly, cup. It was a real penance to drink it. Every sip was intently watched by the lynx-eyed Indian shopkeeper, who claimed that his life had once rested upon what he kindly termed my skill as a "carving surgeon"! Looking up from his shop, I again read the calico sign, and uttered a pious, though silent, wish, that I had been included as well as the King!

I was invited to the official afternoon tea party. African servants in gold-braided velvet waistcoats served tea under shady trees. All the Europeans in Mpwapwa were there. Hearing that I was an Australian, the Governor's wife very graciously came over and talked with me. It appeared that she, too, was an Australian, *and* a nurse, and that she had actually been a Sister in my training hospital in Sydney.

Of course, we talked shop. She wanted to know who gave my anesthetics, so I told her of our makeshift anesthetic apparatus, which was made from an automobile tire pump, a football bladder, a broken stethoscope, and a pickle jar. She laughed heartily at this, and said:

"But what about your needles and catgut?"

"Oh," I replied, "I do those myself."

"And the sponges and the instruments?"

"An African dresser and his wife manage those between them."

She stared at me.

"Do you mean to say that you are your own anesthetist, and, singlehanded, have to tackle three doctors' work? And all that with only one European nurse to assist?"

Then I told her how often and often sickness, or a difficult obstetric case, robbed me even of the help of the European Sister.

"Doctor, I'd give a lot to scrub up and help you out here. Perhaps the opportunity will come some day."

It was a prophetic utterance.

Actually, my stay in Mpwapwa was to be a brief one. I had arranged to catch the Tanganyika Express, which, rather unkindly, left at three in the morning.

With the aid of an alarm clock, I rose at two.

But the car would not start, and, when it did, two punctures left us in the unhappy position of watching the serpent-like chain of light, which we knew to be the train, meander off from the station, four miles away. The next train would leave in three days' time.

I felt my prospects of godfatherhood were rather thin!

Philosophically I watched the train out of sight, and then got back into the car, which, running true to form, refused to start. I curled up in the back seat and went to sleep, to be wakened just after dawn by a cultured

English voice, which inquired if it could be of any assistance. I was only half awake, and murmured that I was disappointed in an ambition — that I had hoped to become a godfather, but had been frustrated by two punctures and the Tanganyika Railways. My questioner proved to be the aide-de-campe to the Governor. In a moment he had the situation under control.

"I am sure His Excellency would be charmed to make seating available for you in the Viceregal train. Just pop your bags into my car, and I'll run you down to the station."

My African houseboy drew my shabby suitcase out of the back of the Mission car. We proceeded in state to the railway station without incident.

I was invited to morning tea, and answered a veritable catechism of questions regarding the people, their problems and their illnesses. It was amazing to me what a comprehensive grasp the Governor had of the tribal life of the people. Just before the buildings of Dodoma came into view, I made my farewells, but the Governor's wife detained me for a moment, and said:

"I'm coming to see that hospital, Doctor, no matter what the official itinerary may be."

From the station I dashed off to the Cathedral, and arrived just in time to name the child.

Back at Mvumi Base Hospital, I found a collection of surgery cases so grotesque that even to speak of some of them would be out of place.

One woman, most aptly named "*Tabu*" which means "Trouble," had been carried in on an upturned native bed. On examination, I found that both her hips were dislocated. Sechelela helped me in the examination.

"*Kah,*" said she, "I have never seen that happen before."

Nor had I, and I didn't like the prospect of trying to replace the dislocations, which obviously had been present for weeks.

"What did you do?" I asked. "Did you fall down a well? Or fight with your husband, or what?"

"Oh, no," said the patient. "It just happened. Yesterday I was well. I went to bed and woke in the morning, and, behold, there was the trouble."

"*Wacho!* — Rot!" said Sechelela, and, turning to me, she said:

"Leave her to me, Bwana. I will find out the truth."

A few minutes later she arrived, with a broad smile.

"Bwana," she said, "thus it is that women suffer when there is no hospital for them. Behold, she has had nine children, and they all died!" To insure that there would be no trouble with the latest, the *wadala* — the female counterpart of the witch doctor — had instructed her husband to grasp her by the ankles, stand on the roof of his mud hut and shake her, head down, with vigor. So successful had this maneuver been that the baby, her tenth, died within a few minutes of its birth, and both the woman's hips were dislocated.

For three weeks she lay on a cowskin in the gloom of the insect-infested house, and had contracted both tick and malarial fever. The witch doctor had "made medicines." Goats' fat and astringent herbs apparently were the main ingredients, but his enterprise had produced no helpful effect.

When the husband felt that his wife was going to die, he brought her to the hospital.

When Sechelela finished her story, I shook my head, and pictured the physical and mental agony of that unfortunate woman, brooding over her lost infants, and suffering torments from her dislocated hips, lying helpless and hopeless in the dark stuffiness of the native house.

Quinine and arsenic injections were given to deal with the fevers. Regular meals and concentrated tonics built up her physique until one day I felt she was fit to be dealt with. So I screwed pulleys into the rough-cut beams of the roof above her bed.

"*Kah,*" said the junior nurse, "what are those for? Are you going to hang people, Bwana?"

"Yes," I said, "junior nurses who do not sweep under the beds, and who break thermometers."

This was greeted with great enthusiasm from the patients.

Then Daudi arrived with a chloroform bottle. A quarter of an hour later, the regular breathing of the patient was my signal to go ahead. Even under deep anesthesia, it took me two hours to replace those grossly swollen hips. One of the happiest sensations that I have ever experienced was to hear the click of that second thigh going back into position.

As she came out of the chloroform, she rolled about in bed groaning, and then, as realization dawned upon her, she exclaimed.

"*Kah!* They are unlocked!"

And grimacing with pain, she gingerly bent her knees. For a week she swallowed aspirin and had daily rubbings and massage.

And then the pulleys came into use. Ropes were strung through them, bandages put around her knees, and she was placed in such a position that, by pulling the ropes gently, she could exercise her damaged limbs. It was most amusing to watch her at this. Gradually the swelling subsided, and she learned to walk again.

At first, she could walk only with sticks, then she moved from pillar to pillar on the veranda, and at last she walked home, armed with a dozen aspirin tablets tied in a corner of her cloth and a catsup bottle filled with liniment.

Since then she has been a most regular visitor at the hospital. One morning I saw her whispering very earnestly with Sechelela and nodding in my direction. Soon I had the whole story.

After ten pregnancies she had no living child, and was most eager for us to help her. We gave her a series of injections, and she swallowed medicines galore, and followed minutely all our directions. Months later, I saw her returning triumphantly to her village with a nine-pound living, healthy baby.

"Where did you steal that child from?" I asked.

She laughed. "He is mine, my only son."

Sechelela's head appeared out of a window. She frowned at my patient.

"Remember, you! If you want to keep him, no gruel till he has teeth."

Work went on. Plans for rebuilding the hospital occupied all my spare time when I was not engaged in what seemed an endless procession of babies, or in producing barrels of cough mixture and liniment.

Time was so utterly full that I had almost forgotten the Viceregal incident. Then, one Sunday morning, my cook came to the door.

"Bwana, there is a motorcar coming. It is not a Mission car. It is much too good, and it has a flag flying on it."

The first drum had just been beaten for church. I could see the hospital nurses just entering the building, and I knew that the work was being maintained by a skeleton staff. I sent a feverish message to the hospital.

"The Bwana Governor is coming. He wants to see the hospital. Go to it!"

Daudi disappeared in a cloud of dust. Sure enough, it was the Governor and his party.

I left instructions that church services be postponed, plied my visitors with cake and tea, and talked as long as possible to allow as much time as I could for the staff. When we did arrive, nurses and dressers were in spotless uniforms, and the wards were as I have seldom seen them. Not a thing was out of place. Not a sign existed of the disorder that I knew must have existed ten minutes before. Daudi whispered in my ear:

"Bwana, whatever you do, do not enter the dressing room!"

I managed to peep in there quickly while the Sister was telling of her adventures with a cobra that appeared simultaneously with an obstetric emergency. Never have I seen such a show as that dressing room provided. Dishes, soiled linen, mats, three beds — in fact, everything not up to A-1 standard had been hastily bundled in.

Sitting on the floor, in the middle of the debris, were two patients who had refused to wash, and were considered by the dresser not to be *ndigwa ya meso* — food for the eyes. Everything in the hospital was viewed with the greatest of interest, the Governor's wife being especially taken with the maternity work, which later gained our hospitals international reputation.

With a feeling of relief that all had gone so well, I watched the Viceregal party drive off over the plains. The church service started an hour late, and, as we came out, Daudi came to me and said:

"Bwana, truly today was a real parable. We were not fully prepared for the Governor's visit. I hope that it will teach me constantly to be ready to face my Master, Jesus Christ, at any time, without having to bundle away a lot of things, that I am ashamed of, in any convenient hiding place."

CHAPTER 4

We Build, Under Difficulties

STANDING in the shade of a giant baobab tree, I took off my helmet and looked at the hospital. For nearly a year I had been wondering what this jungle hospital would look like. Somehow, my ideas were tinged with what I had been used to in Australia: long, cool corridors; tiled bathrooms; quiet wards, with white-capped nurses hovering hither and thither; operating rooms, with their elusive smell of ether and antiseptic, shining with polished chromium work, glassware and porcelain basins; neat shelves of drugs and dressings; and an operating table that would do anything if you flicked the right lever. But here I was in Tanganyika, looking at what was soon to become the C. M. S. Base Hospital.

The first building I saw was the men's ward, made from sticks tied together with bark and plastered inside and out with mud. This had been whitewashed, but even that did not hide the fact that it was nothing but wattle and daub. Then I looked at the windows. More properly described, they were window spaces shuttered with the bottoms of kerosene boxes. Cautiously, I looked through the door into the gloom beyond. Nothing was visible. The windows were shut, to keep out the driving dust. I stepped in hopefully and bumped into a pole that was helping to keep up the mud roof. I side-stepped, and there was a yell from a patient's relative who was sitting on the floor. I moved hastily to one side, and over went a bedside locker, made from two kerosene boxes. At last my eyes became accustomed to the gloom. It was depressing to see how shortness of funds had produced a ward that was little better than a native hut. At home there would have been a royal to-do if it had been used even as a veterinary hospital.

Thankfully, I stepped outside and blinked in the glare of the blazing, vertical sun. Standing back, I looked at the roof. It was of dried mud, and here and there weeds grew incongruously, poking their leaves between sheets of corrugated iron that were kept in place by great stones. At the far end of this ward was a room that had been used for heating water. The prevailing east wind had eroded a hole in the wall. Eddies of dust came through it. And this was the room that I had to use for urgent operations!

Things came to a head a week later. I was in the men's ward dressing an ulcer as big as the palm of my hand. Beside me, on a kerosene box, was a tray with various bowls of antiseptic, sterilized cotton wool, gauze, and the like. I had removed the dressing. The patient carefully kept the flies at a distance. I was just about to put the dressing in position when I heard a splash. I looked round, and there, in the middle of my bowl of lotion, was a clod of earth as big as a walnut, that had fallen from the roof. I looked at it in disgust.

"Stone the crows!" I growled. The patient couldn't understand a word, but he turned to me and made sympathetic noises. Something, I felt, must be done. We must build a ward that was at least safe, but to try to do everything at once would have meant nothing done properly. As Daudi said, quoting a vivid Gogo proverb, "Slowly, slowly. The dog that hurried produced blind pups."

So I set to work to get a grip of the language. Everywhere I went I carried a list of verbs, mumbling over the syllables to myself as I walked to and from hospital. Another list was propped up against the sugar basin as I tried to masticate Tanganyikan chicken! I even had a list stuck on to my shaving mirror, but still everything seemed to be just a wierd jumble of sound.

Gradually, I sorted out words and phrases and began to understand some of the queer things that Africans say in describing their symptoms. I thought my ears were playing me false one morning, when an old woman informed me that she was the possessor of a restless snake! I called for Daudi.

"Daudi! Surely my ears are blunt today. I think this old woman said that she had a restless snake inside her!"

"Quite right, Bwana."

"Well, go and get me a stick. I'll fix it!"

The African threw back his head and laughed.

"She means, Bwana, that she has indigestion. It's the African way of putting it."

On another occasion, a small boy informed me that his stomach was biting him, which is the polite way for a small boy to express the same thing. A fully grown man, on the other hand, may tell you that his interior jumps! It is all very confusing.

Those were hard days.

Everything was of necessity makeshift. Kerosene tins and kerosene boxes provided us with nearly everything in the way of furniture and hardware. Tools from the car, hammered out sheets of corrugated iron for splints, a sterilized steel knitting needle and molded portions of an old iron bedstead, all played their part in dealing with fractures!

But makeshift proved costly in efficiency and in life.

When I was reasonably settled into my house and had a smattering of the language, I went one morning to talk over the new building with Elisha, our clubfooted carpenter. The African licked his pencil reflectively, and wrote sundry things on a long shaving that he picked up from the floor. He looked up at me.

"We will want twenty *debes*, Bwana."

Now, a "*debe*" is a kerosene tin.

"What for?" I asked.

"We will need much water for the mixing of cement, and Bwana, we will need twelve hammers, six crowbars, two very large hammers for the quarry men, twenty pounds of nails, and fifteen barrels of cement."

I jotted these things down.

"Yes, Elisha."

"Then we will want a dozen dishes so that men may carry sand up from the river, and I have mended the old barrows. They will help in this, too."

We spent hours together, calculating how much stone, how many sun-dried bricks, barrels of cement and tons of corrugated iron it would require. There were still four months of the dry season — ample time for the sun to bake our bricks hard. I let out a contract to a cheerful, woolly-headed individual called Assani. He would make and deliver one hundred sun-dried bricks on the job for a shilling. Then I heard of a native merchant whose *go-down* — storage shed — had been blown over by a hurricane. We hastened to buy the material, stipulating that the Indian should supply solder sufficient to mend all the holes. We sent men into the forest to cut timber for scaffolding. Others carried sand from the river.

But the thing that cheered me most was the help given by the boys and girls from the C.M.S. Schools. They said they wanted to do their part in building up a place of healing. The girls went to the river and carried up stones on their heads for the operating room. The boys did likewise, but carried them on their shoulders, the girls, of course, carrying the bigger ones! This is as it should be, since women carry the heavy loads; they are more fitted for it! I was surprised to see fourteen-year-old girls carrying a stone that I could barely lift. I went to watch how they did it. Five or six of them would lift the stone; the one who was to carry it coiled her cloth into the shape of a doughnut and put it on her head. Carefully it was balanced, and then away she went to carry her contribution to the building. Soon a great pile of stone stood near the site.

We set masons to work facing stone. Four stalwarts quarried granite for the foundations. Soon we were ready to build. With Elisha's help, I made out a list of the workmen. Every man had his ticket, and on each ticket the days that he worked were recorded. Wages were fixed, and we were ready to build a hospital for four hundred pounds! It seemed to me at first like a conjuring trick, producing laboratories out of a top hat — like rabbits!

But I found it could be done. Carefully, we laid the foundations. I had to check everything — proportions of sand and cement for the concrete work — the square of the building, and, hour by hour, I prowled around, between operations and hospital rounds, to make sure that the work was going on. Ten strong men, walking one behind the other, carried great dishes of sand on their heads from the river. Another group transported great rough chunks of stone from the quarry. Still others carted stone for the concrete work. We had two months before the rains would come, and so we placed great piles of mud-brick readily accessible. The carpenters prepared doors and window-frames, battens, rafters and plates.

My knowledge of carpentry was increasing by leaps and bounds. Elisha was tireless — going from group to group, but, when he went back to his carpenter's shop, the masons started to take things easy. I badly needed an overseer. I was trying to be a doctor, and five different varieties of specialist, as well as builder and foreman. Little wonder that I longed for some competent African to help. Elisha was good in his way, but two of the masons were his relatives, and if he dealt forcibly with them there would be real trouble in his family circle. So he blamed the other masons for his relatives' shortcomings; up went the balloon, and I had to add peacemaker to my other roles.

As the walls went up, I went around twice a day with a spirit level, checking up, because African masons find it all too easy to produce a sloping wall, which is *not* a good thing. When mistakes were made, the wall had to be rebuilt, and great were the grumblings. One mason said: "It is that wretched spirit level. If he hadn't got one of those, he would not know."

Later on in the day, I heard a crash. The mason had — accidentally — knocked it off the shelf. There was elation among the workmen.

"Now he will not know. Now he cannot grumble at us, and make us do the work all over again."

But I had an answer to this, and put up plumb lines. But it was easier to move the plumb lines than to build a straight wall! So I sighed, and supervised more and more.

My real trouble started when the wages were due to be paid. Man after man had some quarrel regarding the days he had worked. I had overlooked one day, or his ticket had been lost! They would stand and argue and argue, knowing that you were so busy that, if they talked long enough, you would probably do what they wanted out of sheer necessity.

I did not confine my activity to building, but also to arranging such modern conveniences as makeshift and the jungle permitted.

Six grunting Africans carried a crate to the hospital. Carefully Elisha opened it, taking the nails out and straightening them, and piling up the wood for use in his later furniture making.

From its packing emerged a shining barrel-shaped affair. The nurses looked at it with open eyes and open mouths.

"*Yoh,*" said Sechelela. "What is this?"

"It's a machine, Sech, to heat water. A few dry corn cobs, and a handful of grass, and *kumbe!* the water is so hot your hands can't go into it."

The staff was really sceptical, and, as the chip heater came into view, I heard a number of varied views as to the effectiveness of the contraption. First came Elisha, now in his element. I assigned him to cut a hole in the corrugated iron roof, and to install the heater in his very best professional manner. When the job was half done I left to see a rehearsal of a hygiene play which the school girls were giving.

I arrived in time to see the first act. There were three girls, all dressed native fashion, and lying in the typical way these people of Central East Africa choose in their own homes. They lie on the floor on a palm tree mat or on a cowskin, and cover themselves as best they can with a cotton blanket.

They lay there, and scratched and scratched and grumbled and grumbled. Their dialogue was most interesting.

"I am bewitched," said one. "I scratch every night. Day is all right, but night, *kah!* How I itch! It's the work of my relatives who say that I caused trouble to their cows. They've made spells."

The second girl broke in: *"Kah!* It's powerful witchcraft. Behold, now I'm cranky and tired. I cannot work properly. My father beats me. He says I'm lazy, but I itch! I scratch!"

The third one came in as a sort of chorus: "I itch! I scratch! I scratch! I itch!"

The curtain found them in a crescendo, proclaiming their theme song.

Act two was very vivid. A small girl with a deep voice was rigged up as a truly fearsome scabies mite. In a shrill giggle, very different from her ordinary tone, she proclaimed:

"I'm the *itch* dudu. I make them scratch. *Yoh!* What fun I have."

The creature then produced the foulest noises from its interior, showed a fearful set of claws and said: "Because I'm small they blame their mothers-in-law. I make trouble in the skin, and in the family." Another burst of fiendish mirth, which stopped with a gurgle as from off stage came the sound of water being carried, and of girlish laughter.

Suddenly a pot of sulphur ointment, pulled by an invisible string, appeared on the stage. The scabies *dudu* had one look at it, gnashed its teeth, and fell foaming on the floor.

The third act disclosed the three girls lying on native beds. They were talking before going to sleep.

Said the first: "*Yoh!* fancy all our trouble being a little *dudu,* that burrowed under our skin. Behold, that C.M.S. Hospital is a place of wisdom, and the medicines are good."

The others agreed, and went into a truly African discussion of the values of bathing and soap; of the values of a bed they had made themselves, and of all sorts of hygiene side issues.

It really was a great show. I congratulated the school girls, and hurried back to the hospital.

I injected twenty-four lepers, and heard their stories of feeling better after the treatment and good food. Then, on my way to see some new eye cases, I passed the Maternity Ward, where Elisha was finishing his task. The floor was covered with wood shavings. On a high stool was a ten-gallon drum to act as water supply, and this was being filled slowly by our buck-toothed water carrier.

"*Tayari lulu* — ready now, Bwana," said Elisha.

I picked up a handful of shavings and put them into the burner, let the water run a little, and then struck a match, and lighted the shavings.

"Count," I commanded. In Swahili, Elisha counted. I thrust in another handful. Elisha had reached twenty-five when I said: "The water is now very hot."

The carpenter stopped counting and sneered.

"Try it," I urged. "Put your hand under there."

He did with the most obvious scorn. The water poured out. With a yell he jumped back, wringing his hand.

"*Kah!* I'm burned," he gasped.

The staff rocked with joy, and old Sechelela shook her head.

"*Kah,* what a wisdom machine. Behold, there will not be trouble in the middle of the night now. No primuses to pump and prickers to find. *Yoh!* In a minute it's there. Lots of it, with a handful of paper or rubbish."

One day I was helping in the laying of the iron roof when I saw a procession coming up the hill to the hospital. First came a Mugogo, with the inevitable knobkerri held yoke-fashion across his shoulders, while behind him pottered an old woman, and, some twenty yards behind her, wearily came another woman, obviously ill.

"Now, Elisha, see that this *bati* is laid right, one rung overlapping, and don't nail it till I've checked it."

"Yes, Bwana," said the lame carpenter, in Chigogo.

Solomon, the mason, wanted me to put my new spirit level on to the stone wall. He had spent three hours of his own time pulling down and re-laying bricks, and wasn't keen on repeating the performance.

I went to the dispensary and washed the signs of toil from my hands.

The patient was blind in one eye, and as thin as a rake. The Sister unwound four native garments, and we were confronted with a huge abdominal tumor.

"*Heya!* — Yes!" said the relatives. "She has had it for two years, but the *Waganga* — witch doctors — and the *Wadala* — village midwives — could do nothing, and now she is very weak. Perhaps she could try your medicine."

I made a diagnosis, and told the relatives that, without an operation, she would most certainly die. There was just a chance of saving her.

A week later we operated, in an ill lighted, stuffy, mud-brick room, with inexperienced African assistants and a terrified African anesthetist. Both our European Sisters were down with malaria. After three hours of intricate surgery, I removed a tumor that filled a hand basin and weighed fifteen pounds. Threading your own needles and groping for your own instruments does not make for speedy surgery. It was the first time I had performed this operation, and, as generally happens with native patients, every possible complication was present.

Her convalescence was stormy. For two days she was in jeopardy. Then she passed twenty feet of tapeworm and made an uninterrupted though slow recovery. After seven weeks of careful nursing, she was ready to go home.

When her husband arrived to fetch her, he started to haggle about the "thank you." (A shilling a week is charged for food, and the operation fee is five shillings.) I heard Sister Banks explaining all this, and then the husband said:

"But, Bibi, twelve shillings is very much. Will you not take five?"

"*Kah!*" said Mwendwa, a nurse who had assisted at the operation, "is your wife worth only the price of one goat?"

"I am a very poor man," replied the husband. "I have only five shillings."

"*Wacho!*" gibed Mwendwa. "Am I a stranger to your village? You have thirty cows, I know."

Everyone laughed and started to talk at once, until, from my vantage point on the roof where I was soldering gutters, I heard the Sister's voice raised in righteous indignation:

"Call the Doctor, and I will get him to put the *ipu* — tumor — back!"

Consternation was followed by roars of laughter, and the husband produced the cash from the corner of his grimy cloth.

Medical work is forceful, practical preaching. I took Peteka, the patient, aside, and said:

"Well, so your *ipu* is gone. Where is it now?"

"It is down the big hole, Bwana."

"Could you get rid of it yourself?"

"No, Bwana."

"Could the witch doctors get rid of it?"

"No, Bwana. But you know how to remove *ipus* and you were able to do it for me."

"Listen, Peteka. What about your sins?"

"Yes, Bwana, I learned about that, too. Sechelela told me; she explained that my sin was like an *ipu;* it made life miserable and killed my soul slowly."

Turning her one good eye upon me, she spoke very softly:

"Taking my *ipu* away hurt me very much, but taking away my sin wounded the Lord Jesus. I was amongst those for whom He died."

I watched the family walk through the hospital gate. Daudi stood by my elbow.

"Bwana," said he, "truly your little knife preaches a Gospel everyone can understand."

There was a sequel to this. Turn the calendar ahead two years and you find me standing away from my car, looking without enthusiasm at a rear axle housing half hidden in thick black clinging mud.

"*Yah,* Samson!" I said. "We will never get out of that by ordinary means. Manpower is needed — a whole lot of people to pull and push and drag. We've got to get home this evening. There are operations to be done at dawn, and here we are — twenty miles from the hospital, a thunderstorm brewing, and we're bogged, utterly bogged."

Samson nodded his head. "Bwana, I will go to the north, and look for people. You go to the south. I only hope we meet some people upon whom we've operated, or given medicine. They will always help."

I put my helmet on the back of my head and walked off in the sweltering heat of an early Tanganyikan afternoon. Along a narrow path through the thornbush I suddenly overheard women's voices. In a river bed was a group of women and girls round a well. One of them had just adjusted a great five-gallon pot of water on her head, and was about to move off when I came on the scene.

"*Mbukwenyi* — Good morning."

"*Mbukwa,* Bwana."

"*Wali waswenu wose?* — Is everybody well?" I asked.

"*Cili waswanu du* — We are all well," they replied. "But who are you who speak Chigogo, our language?"

The woman with the pot of water on her head gently lowered it to the ground.

"*Yoh,*" she said, "do you not know? He is the doctor from the C.M.S. Hospital. Behold, he is a real doctor. His medicines work, and he takes away pain. Truly he has the help of God in his work."

A hush fell on the people, and they looked at me.

"Truly," I replied. "My work is to help people, and I do it because I love God, and would follow His words."

"Yes," said the woman, putting her pot in the sand, so that it would not topple over. "Don't I know it!" Then, turning to me, she said: "Bwana, don't you recognize me?"

Now, her face was vaguely familiar, but when you see some twenty thousand new faces a year, you can imagine my mental card index was not up to the strain, so I said:

"Your face is familiar, but your name! No, I can't remember it."

The woman came closer, and tapped me on the shoulder with her finger.

"*Gwe,*" she said, "you don't remember me? *Kah!*" There was disgust and unbelief in her tone. "Bwana, did not those of the hospital say words that made the whole village laugh for weeks, and did you not preach words that can never be forgotten by me and by many others?"

I was completely at a loss, so I made appropriate noises which were very non-committal and did not satisfy her.

"*Yah!*" she said. "You don't remember."

Now African women have simple tastes in clothing. They wear two cloths, each about three yards long. The first one they wrap around their waist, and tuck in; the second one they wrap around higher up, and tuck in under the armpit. Imagine my horror and surprise when, without a moment's warning, both of these garments were pulled off by their enthusiastic wearer, to reveal an enormous scar of the variety known as neck-to-knee.

"Now, Bwana, do you remember?"

"*Yoh!*" I said, "I remember all right. You're Peteka. Didn't I remove a tumor that just filled a kerosene tin?"

"*Yoh!*" she said, appeased at last, and to my great relief tucking in her clothing again. There was a chorus of enthusiastic grunts from the other women at the well.

"Yes," said Peteka, "the Bwana gave me sleep medicine. I felt no pain, and when I woke up my *ipu* was gone, and the Bwana had sewn me up as I have shown you."

I felt it was my turn, so I said: "Yes, those were the days when I could not speak Chigogo. I had just arrived in your country."

"*Yoh!*" said Peteka, "you did not need to speak. Your work told its own story and you pointed me to God."

Then she turned to me. "Bwana, what are you doing here in the bush, miles from your home and your hospital?"

"*Yoh!*" I said. "I am in trouble! My car is stuck deep in the mud. I need much help — many people who will push and pull."

"*Kah!* Bwana, a little thing like that! We'll get you out."

They did.

Soon, along the path, in single file, came men, boys, small boys, and very small boys. Samson had hitched a rope on to the front axle. Heading the battalion of aid was the C.M.S. teacher, wearing a threadbare shirt in the tail-out vogue of the country. He gripped my hand.

"Bwana," said he. "It is with joy that we help you out. The people of C.M.S. are our friends, our counsellors, and our helpers. Shall we not help too?"

The next ten minutes were employed in most constructive mud slinging. Branches of trees were laid down as a sort of a track to give the wheels some grip, and when we felt everything was ready, I got into the car. Samson cranked, and the engine spluttered into life.

"When you hear the voice of the car," I yelled, "then push, and those on the rope, pull. Keep her moving, whatever you do; keep her moving, till we get out of the black mud."

"*Ale, viswanu, Bwana,*" came from all sides.

I shifted into low gear, and blew the horn. The engine roared, my helpers grunted or sang. Then came a yell from behind, and — we moved! Frantic pushing and pulling marked our progress. I glanced into the rear view mirror and saw a very amusing sight — a group of small boys, wiping sticky black mud from their eyes. They had been standing behind the car, making helpful remarks but doing little else. With the furious turning of the wheels the mud had been thrown up, catching them fairly in the face. The car slew violently, but we continued to progress until at last we were on firm ground. Lightning was flickering over the hills, and thunder rumbled ominously. I got out and shook hands. The last of my helpers was Peteka. She took my hand in hers, and put it to her lips.

"Bwana," she said, in a low voice. "I can never tell you what your help meant. Life is a new thing."

"Peteka," I replied, "I can help you only for a little time in this world. But the One who is your Chief and mine — the Son of God — He is the One who keeps us here and in the hereafter."

She nodded. "Bwana, I do not cease to tell the story of what you did for me, and how it made me understand what He did for me."

"Bwana," called Samson. "Hurry! It's going to rain."

I waved goodbye and as we bumped along our way to the jungle hospital, I said:

"There, a life saved, a village contacted, a school started, and a hundred friendly and helpful people, and the whole thing at the cost of four gallons of gasoline."

"*Yoh!*" said Samson. "So I don't wonder, Bwana, that you often walk."

At last the buildings were finished. Floors were cemented, walls whitewashed, and the rooms were occupied gradually.

In triumph Daudi carried his microscope, test tubes and stains to the new pathology room. The new dispensary's shelves were lined with bottles by Samson and his perspiring junior. Judith arranged her baby scales and tacked up pictures of how and how *not* to feed a baby, in the welfare room. Yamusi wanted me to see the bathroom window which had been put in upside down and gave passersby a fine view of its cemented floor. Altogether, everyone was highly delighted with the new buildings.

The dressers invited me to a housewarming in their new quarters. After a native feast, they entertained me with some of their tribal games.

A week later the operating room was ready. Shelves and instrument cupboards had been made with packing cases, and the stone room, with its cement plastered walls and glass shelves, shone with instruments and stainless steel bowls and dishes that I had brought from Australia. The newly-enamelled operating table and the anesthetic traymobile, with its array of bottles and mouth gags, made a most imposing show.

"*Kah,*" said Daudi, "it's grand, now we can operate with safety."

I nodded, and felt a glow of internal satisfaction that I should have recognized as a dangerous symptom.

CHAPTER 5

We Rebuild

I WAS feeling complacent about the hospital. It looked splendid, with its whitewashed walls and newly polished doors. Everything was spotless. I walked round the place, purring to myself! Blissfully unconscious of the trouble that lay ahead, I walked into the surgery and grinned, as I looked at the window — a highly patchwork affair, made from pieces of glass of all different sizes. It was not a thing of beauty, but it certainly let in the light. I gazed at the ceiling. That, at any rate, was all right. It was made from special plywood, guaranteed to be white-ant-proof. To check this, we had put it, for a fortnight, on a white ant's nest. The ants had scorned it. And there it was, a splendid reflecting surface. At last we could operate in a proper room, without fear of dust and *dudus* — as insects are called in Tanganyika.

I peered down the two great underground tanks. They had twenty thousand gallons in them — enough water to last us for three months. I turned to Daudi.

"Surely, Daudi, the hospital's grand now. Everything is as we planned it."

"Yes," said Daudi. "The laboratory's excellent, and your idea for a sink was splendid."

The bottom had broken off a huge glass bottle, so we upended it and used it as a sink. Wood from gasoline cases had been used for cupboards, for tables, for test tube racks, and for all the incidentals of our jungle laboratory. Everything was in its place, and I went home with a warm feeling of a job well done. It had been hard work, but it was worth it all.

And then the rains came. Gently at first, and we went round adjusting gutters and pipes. Water was so valuable that we were not willing to lose even a bucketful. I listened to the music of the water running into the wells, and when I lowered a dipstick, they were two-thirds full. I chuckled with glee to myself. What a change from carrying every drop of your water in kerosene tins from the wells a mile and a half away!

Sechelela, the old matron, was amusing herself planting peanuts in part of the hospital garden.

"Bwana, I have a feeling there is trouble in the air."

"*Wacho* — not a bit of it," I replied. "They are holding every drop. They're splendid tanks."

"*Kah,*" said Sechelela, "I can feel trouble in my bones."

"Take some aspirin," I replied. "It's your rheumatism again."

She leaned on her hoe, and laughed at me.

"You will learn," she said. "You will learn."

And that night, I did! There was a terrific thunderstorm, in the middle of which I was nearly thrown out of bed by a brisk earthquake shock. At daybreak Samson was on my doorstep.

"Bwana, both the tanks are cracked, and the water's running out fast."

I hurried up to the hospital. One tank was empty, and the other had just a foot of water left. Three months' supply gone in an hour!

We looked at each other in dismay.

"And they are only little cracks, Bwana," said Samson.

I nodded.

"Bwana, it teaches us a big thing. Little sins kill a man's soul just as readily as big sins."

"Truly, Samson. We will tell them about that this morning at prayers. It is better to find a parable in things like this than to moan about them."

Stephano, the mason, arrived with a ladder. He probed the cracks and packed them with cement.

"It should not leak again now, Bwana," said he.

"Huh," said Samson. "That does not bring the water back."

Mhutila, the one-eyed water carrier, spat viciously into the incinerator.

"*Kah,*" said he. "What a waste of water! *H-e-e-e-e-e,* surely we are unfortunate. *Bahati mbaya* — very bad luck."

And that was the beginning of troubles. Two days later, Daudi arrived at the door.

"Bwana, come and look at our surgery. Oh, Bwana . . ."

"What's up, Daudi? Why do you look so miserable?"

He just shook his head, and walked dejectedly in front of me. What a wreck the whole place was! The white ants had eaten the white-ant-proof ceiling, and there was mud, white ants and plywood, all over the floor. Our shining bowls and dishes were filled with mud. The whole place looked like a bombed-out city. We cleaned it up, and proceeded to put up a new ceiling, this time of non-corrugated iron.

"*Kah,*" said Elisha viciously, as he hammered in a nail. "This will blunt the white ants' teeth!"

Daudi grinned. We went outside together.

"Well, Daudi," I said. "What can happen next? Hurricanes, earthquakes, whirlwinds, thunderstorms . . . ."

"We haven't been struck by lightning yet, Bwana!"

Nor were we. But trouble came from another quarter. A plague of cockroaches invaded wards and stores. I felt like Pharaoh. You opened a door, and down they came in a cascade on your head! There were cockroaches in the linen cupboard; pull out a towel and a dozen cockroaches would follow it in formation. You had to skim them off the hand basin before you could wash your hands. They fell in the medicines, crawled over beds and patients, scampered over the floor; in fact, you heard the crunch, crunch, crunch of cockroaches at every step you took. We boiled buckets of water and sprayed everything. The staff was armed with Flit-guns, and we fumigated and scraped, dusted pyrethrum, and waged incessant warfare on the brutes. Yohanna, the gardener, took kerosene tinfuls of cockroaches and buried them in his garden. I watched him covering them up.

"Burying them, Yohanna?"

"Yes, Bwana, they're grand manure."

Sechelela had an even more optimistic report. She remarked:

"Oh, well, Bwana, it might be worse. You know, no bug can live while there is a cockroach about."

I took her up on this point.

"Oh, yes, Sech, but cockroaches crawl all over you. Ugh! . . ."

"Let them crawl," she said, "as long as they don't bite."

After a week we were almost back to normal. Mhutila had made a sort of net, with which he scooped three kerosene tinfuls of cockroaches, and one live snake, from the wells one morning. That was the first of the snakes. On and off we had had a few snakes around, but the year's heavy rainfall had encouraged the ground rats, which, in turn, encouraged the snakes.

I was in my office, working on statistics. This is a necessary but trying pastime, when you have to read the queer handwriting of some of these folks. I roared for Samson, for Daudi, for Kefa. No one appeared. A confused noise near the store drew me out to investigate. There were the dressers, each with a stick, in a circle around a hooded cobra that was sitting up and spitting viciously at them. The men were returning the compliment by spitting at the snake, while one after the other lunged at it with his stick. Kefa suddenly flung his knobkerri with all his force, and the cobra fell, hard hit. Immediately a dozen other sticks whacked him lifeless. Everyone was delighted at the victory, but all agreed that we would see more snakes.

Sechelela killed one that she found in the linen cupboard. Another was discovered coiled around a table leg in the men's ward, while Yohanna killed six in his gardens.

One morning I was in the surgery getting some instruments together for a surgical operation. I was thinking about the ceiling and white ants, when something caused me to look down, and there, not six feet away, was a young cobra, looking at me in a distinctly hostile fashion. That was more than I could tolerate, so I beat a tactful retreat, and got hold of a bottle of spray-on anesthetic. For fully thirty seconds the reptile and I were engaged in a duel, but the enemy was outranged. It swayed to and fro, and then collapsed on to the floor, anesthetised. I jumped for a pair of plaster shears, and amputated its ugly head — to me, a very successful operation, the surgeon being more than content, even though the patient failed to survive.

I felt this, surely, was the last page in a long chapter of accidents, but one evening a seventy mile an hour hurricane ripped its way across the plains, tearing trees up by the roots and sending before it a great cloud of red dust. With a roar, it was on the hospital. There was a crashing of tortured corrugated iron, and five minutes after it was all over I found the men's ward had lost two-thirds of its roof. The dressers had to walk a quarter of a mile into the valley to recover the iron.

Elisha mustered his forces. The iron was put back temporarily, and great stones placed on top of it. I felt distinctly glum. Surely, I was the most amateur of builders, but there was some measure of comfort in hearing that the Dodoma Railway Station had lost, not only its roof, but part of its top story.

I have always made it a rule to look for a reason in these happenings. I helped hand up the stones to the carpenters, as they put the roof back into shape, and then I went around to see how the patients were getting on. In one ward were two Africans, both cripples. One, a Masai, had nearly recovered and could walk about, but the other had both legs encased in plaster of Paris. As the hurricane tore off the roof, the first man jumped screaming beneath his bed, and lay there shivering with fright for the best part of an hour. The other lad lay calmly in bed, making no fuss, and obviously free from panic of any sort. He spoke to his roommate, and told him the danger was over. The roof certainly had gone, and one piece of corrugated iron had crashed between the beds, making a considerable hole in the concrete floor. James, the cripple, was, incidentally, a first-class woodcarver. His very artistic work adorned the Cathedral at Dodoma. He was a very definite Christian, and carried his belief in Jesus Christ into his everyday doings.

"*Yah,*" said the man as he emerged from under the bed, "I thought my last hour had come. I felt sure I would be cut in half by that piece of *bati*. *He-e-e-e-e,* did not the wind scream like a thousand devils?"

"Yes," said James, "it did; but I am not afraid of a thousand devils, because I know Jesus Christ. I am not frightened to die, because I know that Jesus is waiting for me on the other side. I am His son."

"How do you know that?" said the other man.

"I read it in God's Book. He says, 'Him that cometh to Me, I will in no wise cast out.' I came to Him. I asked Him to take away my sin, and He did. All the rules of the Christian tribe are in this Book." He pointed to a dilapidated New Testament beside his pillow.

"*Yah,*" said the man, "and, truly, has that taken from you the fear of death?"

"Well," said James, "I am not under the bed, am I?"

A fortnight later, I shook hands with the Masai as he went home. He said:

"Bwana, I have real reason to thank you. Behold, my legs now are straight, and work. And, Bwana, I have started to learn about Jesus, who takes away the fear of death."

"Yes," I said, "there is wisdom in that. Does not Jesus give us everlasting life, which starts now?"

"Truly, Bwana, and I will learn of these things from the C.M.S. School in our village."

I said good-bye to him, and made an entry in the hospital inpatient register. He had been in six weeks. We had operated twice. We had fed, clothed and treated him, and the total cost had been twelve shillings, six pence. It was worth all of the difficulties — be they cockroaches, earthquakes, white ants, or hurricanes — to see what I had seen, and hear what I had heard, that afternoon.

CHAPTER 6

Fleas and Fungus

I SAT on a stool made from a kerosene box, in our surgery which had cost one hundred and twenty pounds. My shoe and sock were off, and my foot was on the table. Daudi had iodined the toe that was to be operated upon, and was scrubbing his hands before dealing with my *funza*. He was giving me a lecture.

"You know perfectly well, Bwana, you shouldn't walk around without your shoes on. As surely as you do, the *funzas* will get into your toes, and then there'll be trouble."

"I'll try to be good, Daudi," I laughed, "but it's very hard to find your shoes when you're called in the middle of the night and you're half asleep, and you can't light the hurricane lantern, and you try to strike the wrong end of the match."

The dresser laughed.

"Have you ever seen a *funza,* Daudi?"

"Yes, Bwana. They are like a tiny little flea, and they live in the dust until they can burrow into somebody's toe and do what they've done to you."

He picked up a long, bayonet-pointed needle and deftly cut away the skin over the red, extremely itchy lump underneath my little toe. He dissected away for a minute or two, then, with a smile of satisfaction, produced the egg sac, that looked like a swollen grain of wheat.

"There it is, Bwana. All in one piece!"

Once again he put iodine into the young cavern the *funza* had left in my toe, and proceeded to bandage up.

"It's a very useful custom in our tribe to pierce your ear. Have you noticed, Bwana, how many people have a safety pin, as well as all the other ironmongery and ornaments in their ear lobes?"

"I have seen that frequently, Daudi!"

"That safety pin is their portable operating room for taking out *funzas,* Bwana."

"Kah," I said. "Think of all the germs on it."

"Yes, Bwana, but think how thick their feet are."

As we were leaving the surgery I saw two men carrying a hammock, stretched on a bit of bush timber.

"Kah," said Daudi. "Here's work. Looks like a man, Bwana, because the carriers obviously find it heavy."

The "ambulance" was followed by the usual collection of small boys, who were anxious to miss nothing.

On the concrete veranda outside the men's ward was a circle of interested spectators. When I arrived, the patient was drinking water from a gourd. I greeted everybody:

"Mbukwenyi!"

"Mbukwa, Bwana."

I turned to the lad on the ground. *"Mbukwa."*

"Mbukwa, Bwana," he replied.

"Tell me of your sickness."

"My name is Yamusi Cikata, Bwana. I used to be an out-school teacher at Nghati. One day I noticed a lump on my foot. I had had a *funza."*

Daudi looked at me and grinned!

"I dug it out with my safety pin and thought I must have dug too deeply. Then I noticed more lumps, and soon they started on the other foot."

"Could you still walk, Yamusi?"

"Yes, I could walk, Bwana, but then my feet swelled and got so sore that soon I could only hobble with a stick. I borrowed a donkey and rode fifty miles to the Government doctor, but he could do nothing, so I went home, and my feet got worse and worse. I cannot even stand now, and so I have come to you, because I know that at this C.M.S. Hospital, if you can help me, you will."

I knelt down and uncovered his feet. They were twice their normal size. He was suffering from Madura Foot, a foul fungus disease. Both his feet were covered with crater-like warty growths. Daudi disappeared in the direction of his small laboratory. He returned in a minute or two with a glass rod and some slides. He took several drops of fluid from one of the open sores, put them on the slides, and went to see what he could find under the microscope. Yamusi was carried into the ward, bathed, and put to bed. A little later I came to give him a complete examination. My findings were rather grim. The disease had made considerable headway, and both his legs were affected.

"Bwana, can you help me?"

"Yes, but the disease is very bad indeed. The only way to save your life will be to cut both your legs off above the knee."

The lad's face fell. "But, Bwana, there's no place for a man in our tribe who has no feet. Is there no medicine that can cure my feet?"

I shook my head doubtfully.

"How can I cultivate, Bwana? How can I look after my garden, and my cattle, if I cannot walk? A man without feet is utterly useless."

"Yamusi," I said, "I know of no other way."

"The Bwana doctor at Dodoma told me the same words. But I thought that perhaps you could help me more, because you, like myself, are a Christian."

He pulled a worn Testament from his cloth, and said:

"Bwana, you do believe in God, don't you?"

"I do, Yamusi."

"Do you believe this Book?"

"I do."

"Then read this."

He handed me the Book, but my knowledge of the language was not sufficient for me to translate it. I turned to Daudi:

"Translate it for me into English, will you?"

"The very strong prayer of a man who is right with God is most effective." (In our translation it reads: "The effectual, fervent prayer of a righteous man availeth much.")

"Do you believe that, Bwana?"

"Yes, Yamusi, I do."

"Do you believe it enough to stake my life on it?"

"That depends on you as well. It says in the Book: 'If two of you shall agree in anything that you ask, it will be done.' "

"I believe, Bwana, that God can heal me. I am His son, and so are you, so we have every right to ask."

"Well, let us have faith and ask that He will heal you, Yamusi."

I knelt beside his bed. Together we asked God to heal those feet and to turn His promise into hard fact.

From the purely medical point of view it looked hopeless, but we were not viewing the future from the purely medical point of view. All the usual medicines were given — hot foot baths, injections, and the like, but little progress was made. Yamusi had a piece of string which he kept under his pillow. It was knotted in two places, and showed the circumference of each foot. Each Saturday he measured them.

At the end of six months he still lay there, full of faith and cheerfulness, and doing a stout job in the ward by talking to his fellow patients, and telling them of God. No African resents talking about God, and hour after hour the convalescents sat round his bed, listening and asking questions. The seventh month came, and one morning as I was doing my rounds, I said:

"What story does the string tell today, Yamusi?"

He smiled up at me. "It says, Bwana, that they are no worse. Do you still believe that God can answer our prayers? Because I do."

"Yes, Yamusi, I still believe, but I don't think that we can hurry God in the matter."

The eighth month came. As I stood by his bed, Yamusi produced his string. There were three knots in it.

"Bwana, the swelling is definitely less. See where I have measured it. That was last month." He showed me the knot in the string. "But now it's here."

We knelt beside his bed and thanked God for the small amount of improvement, and asked for more. Week by week more knots appeared in the string.

"Behold," said Yamusi, viewing his lower limbs, "they are beginning to look like feet again."

One morning I found him hobbling around the ward. He was positively beaming. Before the year was up, he was able to walk without a stick, and without pain. He came to me in the office one morning.

"*Mbukwa,* Bwana."

"*Mbukwa,* Yamusi."

"Bwana, I am cured, and I want to tell you that this is as surely the work of God as anything that happened in the New Testament."

"Truly," I said. "God certainly answered our prayers and you are going home now, Yamusi?"

"I have no home, Bwana. Let me live here and be a dresser in the hospital. Let me show my thankfulness for what God has done for me by helping my fellows. I understand sickness so much better than the others, because I have suffered pain."

"Can you do the job, though, Yamusi? Don't you think it will be too much for you?"

"I don't think so, Bwana. I have been helping for two months now. At any rate, if I get too tired, I am close to you and I can get help and tonics. I think I can do it, and I'll see that medicines are given out at the proper time, and I know how it feels not to have your bed made and not to be bathed. Please, Bwana, give me a trial, at least."

I agreed, and soon his value was apparent. He was kindness itself to his patients.

I don't want you to think our hospital was a place of success all the time.

A few weeks after Yamusi was put in charge of the ward, Daudi arrived at my house, almost stuttering with excitement.

"Bwana," said he, in English, "a man has arrived after three days' safari, and is at hospital. He has abdomen most very large, huge and colossal. Please, will you view him?"

I smiled at the quaint selection of adjectives and determined to give him some further instruction in English.

For a while Daudi continued in English, but couldn't find words sufficient, so he burst into Chigogo, and told a story that made me all the more keen to see the phenomenon.

I went into the ward, took up the record book to see that all the temperatures were what they should have been, and then went to see our newest arrival. He was completely covered with bedclothes, and had a truly mountainous appearance. Yamusi had a grin from ear to ear.

"*Kah,* Bwana! There was never a man like this before!"

"I hear that he is colossal and immense," I said.

"Yes, Bwana," said Yamusi. "He's all that, and he is lying in bed, with his abdomen beside him!"

"What?" I said.

"You look," said the dresser.

I did, and it was true. I have never seen such a case. All Daudi's adjectives were fully justified. The patient raised what he could of himself on one elbow, and greeted me. I sat and listened to his story.

"Bwana, for many years I have suffered from a restless snake" — by which I knew he meant indigestion — "and for three years now my stomach has become larger and larger. I have swallowed much native medicine. *He-e-e-e-e,* how I vomited, but it did no good. Many poultices have been put upon me, many times have I been scratched. Still I grew larger. For years I hoped, and paid out cattle, but behold, it was useless, and now my cattle are finished, and I could not pay to be carried to this hospital, so I walked."

"What!" I said, "you walked, with that?"

"Yes, Bwana. Three days I walked through the forest."

"Where from?"

"From Cibogolo."

"*Kah,*" said Yamusi. "That is sixty miles by road."

"Well," said the patient, "three times I fell down, and behold, I could not stand up. But people found me, and at last I arrived. Do you think, Bwana, you have the medicine that will help me?"

I looked at Yamusi and nodded.

He replied: "The Bwana has a medicine, and it will help you."

"*Kah,*" said the man. "But I have no cattle left to pay a thankoffering."

"The Bwana does not worry about cattle. He would rather that you learned about God, and about the way of real life. Surely life has not been full of joy when you carry that round with you?"

"*Huh,*" said the man, "I am not one of those who want God. Many times have I heard the teacher tell the story, but it is nothing to me. I don't want it."

"*Ehugh!*" said Yamusi, "would you not be thankful to the Bwana if he helped you?"

"Yes," said the man, "I would, but I'd not feel thankful to God."

I examined the patient, and arranged for an operation next day. His was a case of tuberculous peritonitis. With infinite care we drew off literally buckets of fluid. The man was given rests between these reductions. With great pride, he watched himself becoming more and more normal, but always he had little time for the story of Jesus. The final tapping was performed. Yamusi brought the ward book.

Sixteen gallons have we taken from this man. Now he can walk and is comfortable."

"*Yah,*" said the man. "Am I not normal again? Now I can go and live. I want to drink much beer. I want everything that life has to offer me. Once again I can live, and no one shall stop me. I have been saved from my trouble," he looked defiantly at Yamusi, "and God shall not stop me!"

"God does not want to stop you," said the dresser. "He wants to give you a bigger life. A life that lasts for ever. He wants to free you from your burden and give you a joy that you cannot get out of beer and living like you used to live."

"*Pah . . .*" said the man. "*Wacho*! Not a bit of it!"

That day our patient paraded round the village. He had a photograph that I had taken of him on arrival. He showed this to everyone, and said:

"That's what I was. Now look at me."

Astonishment was expressed on every hand.

"*He-e-e-e,*" said one old man. "You must be thankful to the Bwana and to God!"

"I'm thankful to the Bwana, but not to God. Those dressers did not drink. They did not live loosely, and they even apologized when they told lies. *Kah!* What foolishness. I want to live — and live I shall. I want nothing of God."

"That's dangerous talk," said an old African Christian. "It says in the Book: 'He that hath the Son hath life, and he that hath not the Son of God, hath not life.' "

"*Wacho!* You are an old fool," replied my star patient, and walked off without so much as saying "goodbye," dressed in a pair of hospital pajama trousers, and with a hospital blanket thrown round his shoulders. Just after sunset I went to check up on the temperatures, as usual, but there was no sign of our friend who had been "very enormous and huge."

"*Kah,*" said Yamusi, "he was a thankless person. He has *torokad* — run away — with a pair of pajama trousers, but, fortunately, they were very old and torn, Bwana. *Kah!* He was a trial; nothing pleased him, and he wouldn't listen."

"Well, we can never force anyone to believe. We can only tell them, and if they choose to reject God and all He gives, it's their own affair, not ours."

"Truly, Bwana."

Next morning a native policeman arrived. Our patient had walked eight miles, and had stopped with some relatives close to the house of the chief. They had celebrated his recovery by drinking native mead, brewed from honey, a highly potent drink. Their celebrations had been cut short by the patient who suddenly stood up, as though to make a speech, and then fell back, dead. I called the staff together, and told them of this tragedy. I felt most downhearted about it.

"Well, Bwana," said Yamusi, "we all agree that, while his body was repaired, his mind and his soul were not helped. He was a failure, but think not of the failure, but of the dozens and dozens whom we can help in every way. This work would not be real if we did not have failures."

"Truly," said the old teacher, "I would be dead but for the Bwana, when I had malaria of the brain."

"*Kah,*" said Yamusi, "and I would have died, but for the Bwana treating my feet."

"*He-e-e-e-e,*" said Kefa, "and what about my pneumonia?"

"There you are, Bwana," said Samson. "Do not be downhearted, but let us rather warn people that to turn their backs on God is a very dangerous thing to do."

The ward had taken on a new efficiency under Yamusi's supervision. It used to amuse me to see him, with a long rope, making sure that all the twelve beds in his ward were in an exact straight line. He used to supervise personally the bathing of each new patient, and had very strong ideas about these who came in wearing native mud headdress. He would insist that they should get no food until the whole affair had been cut off. Very few of the patients refused after missing one meal. In the woodshed Yamusi had a fine collection of mud headdresses which he had removed. They were one exhibit that he always insisted on showing visitors when they came into the hospital.

Yamusi carried his Christianity into his everyday job, and it stood the test of a dysentery epidemic. It is utterly contrary to Gogo custom for the people to do any of the unsavory tasks that fall to the lot of the hospital dresser. Nothing but the grace of God or high wages will induce them to deal with what I termed the local "Sewerage and Drainage Board." When the epidemic was at its height, the staff grew restive, and said to Yamusi:

"It's too much to expect us to do this filthy work," and they agreed to come to me and complain. That same morning, at staff prayers, we read from St. John's Gospel the story of the death of Lazarus, and how Jesus gave him back his life. Yamusi went back to the ward, called his helpers together, and said:

"Jesus did not hesitate to go to the grave when He knew that Lazarus' dead body would stink. Cannot I follow my Savior's example and do a few dirty tasks to help others?"

I heard no more from the grumblers.

Months later, I was sitting beside the bed of an operation case. She was one of those who had no will to live. I was doing everything that I knew to save her in a fight that seemed hopeless. I had just poured a pint of a special solution into her veins and given her an injection to make her sleep, when the night nurse tapped me lightly on the shoulder, and whispered:

"Listen, Bwana. Someone has died in the village."

I could hear the wailing of the heathen relatives, long and agonized. The wind whistled round the hospital eerily. There was a staccato bark of a jackal under the baobabs behind the mud and wattle building we used as a mortuary.

I went back to feel my patient's pulse, and was reassured to note its regular beat.

Someone was tapping on the window.

"*Hodi,* Bwana," said a muffled voice.

I went outside. It was Yamusi. He spoke under the stress of great emotion:

"Bwana, my small son has died. He was well an hour ago. He said he had a headache, and went to bed. I came to the hospital for some quinine, and when I returned he seemed asleep. I felt his pulse, and he was dead. The people in the house where I am staying are heathen. Listen — you can hear them wailing now."

On the night wind you could hear the voice of the mourners.

"Bwana, I cannot mourn. Do I not know that God controls everything? Have I not the confidence that one day I will see my small son again?"

CHAPTER 7

German Days and Gala Days

SOME seventy years ago, Stanley traveled through Mvumi, and, according to the story told me by a very old man, he wanted to camp near to where my house now stands. The Wagogo had had repeated battle with the Arab slave traders, and were determined to safeguard themselves against any travelers in caravans, whoever they might be. They were always suspicious of strangers, and asked tremendous sums for even the right to pass through their country unmolested.

The famous explorer was met by the chief, who demanded that a deep hole near his house, especially dug to measure tribute, should be filled with rolls of cloth before Stanley could pitch his camp within his chiefdom. Stanley promptly refused their terms, and went on. I think he probably wrote a portion of his memoirs that night, for in his classic book, *In Darkest Africa,* he states:

> There is no country in Africa that has excited greater interest in me than this. It is a ferment of trouble and distraction, and a vermin of petty annoyances beset the travelers from day to day while in it. No natives know so well how to aggrieve and be unpleasant to travelers. One would think there was a school somewhere in Ugogo to teach low cunning and vicious malice to the chiefs, who are masters in foxycraft. Nineteen years ago I looked at this land and people with desiring eyes. I saw in it a field worth some effort to reclaim. In six months I felt sure Ugogo could be made lovely and orderly, a blessing to the inhabitants and to strangers. Without any very great expense or trouble it would become a pleasant

> highway of human intercourse with far-away peoples, productive of wealth to the natives and comfort to the caravans. I learned, on arrival in Ugogo, that I was forever debarred from the hope. It is to be the destiny of the Germans to carry out this work, and I envy them. It is the worst news of all that I shall never be able to drain this cesspool of iniquitous passion and extinguish the insolence of Wagogo chiefs and make the land clean, healthy and ever-beautiful to view. While my best wishes will accompany German efforts, my mind is clouded with a doubt that it ever will be the fair land of rest and welcome I had dreamed of making it.

He felt that six months would be sufficient to make Wagogo "lovely and orderly," but it has proved to be a very much longer job.

German colonization wasn't a great help. They aimed purely at opening up the country to produce raw materials, regarding the African as a cheap form of labor, and taking little interest in his welfare. They ruled with the whip, the rifle, and the gallows, and took all responsibility out of the hands of the chiefs.

What has been accomplished so far has been made possible by a friendly British administration encouraging the Africans, and by the confidence built up over years by missionaries, who have been able to make very close contacts with the people.

You cannot drag a people from the Stone Age to the twentieth century in one generation. It is unfair, and quite useless, to expect them to change so quickly. They see no need for hurry. Their favorite proverb reads: "Hurry hurry has no blessing." They follow the customs of their forebears, and do not feel inclined to readjust their lives or change their centuries-old customs at one word from us.

In the latter portion of the last century, pioneer missionaries moved in and out amongst the people, learning their languages and customs, sharing their food and gaining their confidences. These men underwent all kinds of hardships and had all manner of narrow escapes, but eventually, by steady, tenacious toil, they won the trust of the people and of the chiefs, and so set the foundation for the work which, in the present day, we are endeavoring to carry on. The African has now learned to cooperate with the Government, and the Government, in turn, judiciously leaves a considerable amount of responsibility in the hands of the African rulers.

The full force of this was brought home to me one afternoon when I had invited the King of Ugogo to afternoon tea, and to listen to the B.B.C. news in Swahili, on my second-hand radio set, which was the wonder of all the people in the district.

Mazengo looked very imposing in his red fez and a khaki *kanzu,* a long nightgown effect, which was embroidered in a lavish, though, to me, not very tasteful, manner. He put the fifth teaspoon of sugar into his tea, stirred it thoroughly, and drank it with audible relish.

The talk drifted on to the days of the German occupation of Tanganyika. The old African clergyman, Mika, a close friend of the chief, who exercised almost as much authority as did Mazengo himself, turned to me and said:

"Bwana, would you like to hear the story of Mazengo's death during the last war?"

"Death?" I said. "He looks very much alive to me."

I looked up just in time to see a teacake disappearing whole into the chief's mouth. "Nevertheless, tell me the story, Mika."

This is what I heard.

In the 1914-1918 war, the German District Officer, Herr Sperling, sent a force of *Askaris* (native soldiers) to capture the chief, dead or alive. Mazengo got wind of this and hid, simply by living as a humble Mugogo, in an ordinary Mugogo's house. Weeks later news came to the fort that Mazengo was dead. He had fled, they said, to the hills, and, while hiding in a cave, had been killed by

Among Those Who Came

AFRICAN JUNGLE AMBULANCE

— two men carrying a hammock, stretched on a bit of bush timber.

". . . an old woman who had fallen off the roof of her house and broken her thigh . . . was carried fifty miles on an upturned bed, to be brought to the [Kilimatinde] hospital. Imagine the agony as her husband and sons carried her for three days in this manner, stumbling through rivers and dense forests!"

(Kilimatinde)

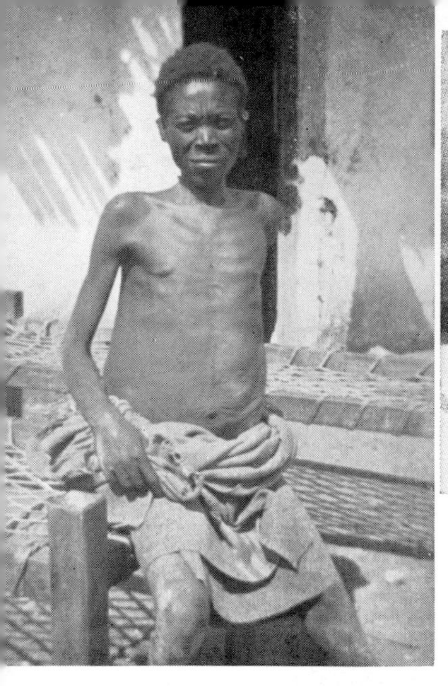

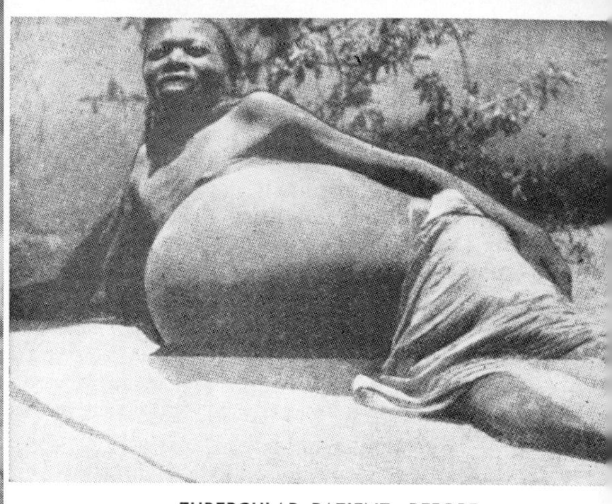

TUBERCULAR PATIENT: BEFORE AND AFTER TREATMENT

Typical of many tuberculous patients in Tanganyika; four kerosene tinfuls of fluid were removed. (Fleas and Fungus)

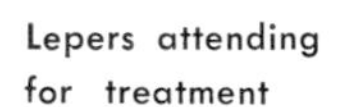

Lepers attending for treatment

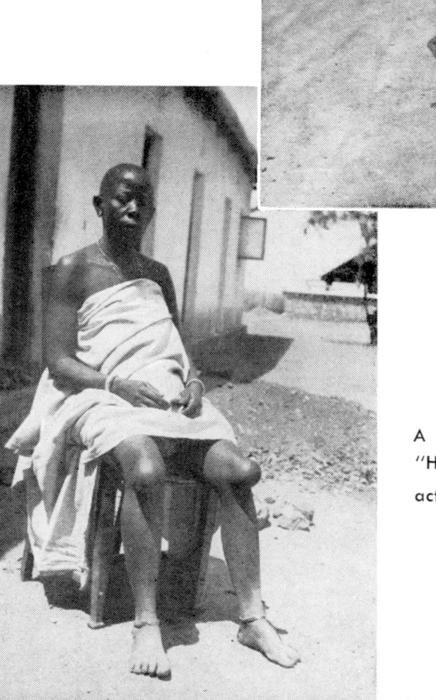

A case of "Housemaid's Knees," actually Tertiary Yaws

a lion. Sperling was dubious, and sent a young lieutenant to view the remains.

The Wagogo had dug a grave, and in it put the carcass of a very dead goat. Under strong protest that it was against their tribal customs to dig up a dead body, they started to disinter the "dead" chief. As they dug deeper and deeper, the still, hot air stank vilely of rotting flesh, while the old women kept up a continuous dirge of "*Yaya gwe!* — Oh, my mother!" — and the white-bearded *Wakombi* — old men — stood silently resentful, watching as the hoes of the diggers turned over the soil.

The stench became unbearable, and, after seeing a muddy mass of putrid flesh and bones, the lieutenant turned away.

"That's Mazengo, all right, not a doubt of it," commented the lieutenant, as he saw a decaying *kanzu* come to light. Not a Mugogo batted an eyelid.

Herr Sperling called the people together at Dodoma and made a speech, in which he told them it was useless to fight against the Germans, for they had God with them.

"Mazengo fled to the forest and was killed by a lion," he said. "This will be the fate of all those who disobey the Kaiser."

"*Ndio,* Bwana, *kweli-kweli* — Yes, sir, very true."

"It is useless to fight against such an Emperor."

"*Kabisa!* — Absolutely!" agreed the crowd.

The Germans returned to the strongly defended fort, satisfied that a tremendous impression had been made on the people, while the Wagogo walked home in single file, over the long, winding tracks through the hills, and laughed and laughed and laughed.

I looked up at the clock as Mika finished the tale. There was still five minutes to go before the broadcast was due. I switched on the set and, seeing the crowd that had assembled outside, carried it out and put it on the well. While the Band of His Majesty's Coldstream Guards played selections from *Iolanthe,* they all stood disgustedly by and criticized the "wyless" and the queer European music. I adjusted the tuning, and, when the tubes howled, many of the audience took to their heels, screaming that it was the voice of the European devils! The rest of the crowd roared with laughter at these timorous ones, who gradually found courage enough to return.

In the "dress circle" were the chief and the African pastor. The latter remarked:

"These Germans said we black men are animals and should be treated as such — and, believe me, they did!"

"How do you mean?" I asked.

"In 1915 they thrashed me and tried to force me to say that Bwana Briggs was signalling to the British troops. When I refused to tell lies, they tied me by my hands to a donkey and dragged me to Dodoma."

"What, pastor, the whole thirty-five miles?"

"Every yard of it, Bwana, and they blinded this eye the same day with a *kiboko* — a hippo-hide whip."

Everyone was silent, and the atmosphere was intensely serious, as the chief said:

"If they return, Bwana, I will take all my family and cattle and go to Portuguese East Africa."

At that moment the selections from Gilbert and Sullivan stopped, and a deep voice said, in their common jargon:

"*Jambo watu wote* — Good day, everybody."

All raised their hats and replied:

"*Jambo sana,* Bwana," and then grinned, realizing that the speaker could not hear them. All were attention now. A little lad who was trodden on in the push for positions, set up a dismal wail, but was quickly hushed.

The chief begged: "Say that again, Bwana," but the radio, unheeding, went on, and this is what we heard:

"Four submarines, ships that travel under the sea like sharks, have been sunk, and our troops are fighting hard on all fronts." The listeners nodded appreciation. "Hitler has made a speech." At the name, all solemnly spat.

The bulletin ended with the announcer's farewell in Swahili, *"Kwaherini,"* and, as the crowd broke up, a big Mugogo, with red mud in his hair, and carrying a long spear, remarked to a lad dressed in khaki shorts and shirt:

"Well, it *is* nice of George to send us news like this. Truly, he is a good King."

The chief shook my hand at the conclusion and thanked me effusively.

"It is very wonderful for us to get news in this way. Please tell your people that I, and my people, stand with King George just as much as they do."

Then he invited me to a *"Siku Kuu,"* held in honor of King George's birthday. We were to be the guests of honor in the absence of His Majesty.

From early morning groups of Wagogo passed our house, dressed in their dance regalia. From our home we could see a haze of dust six miles away. As we came closer we heard muffled shouting and when we actually reached the chief's "palace," the air was thick with dust. Two thousand men and women pounded the ground with their feet in their tribal dances, chanting as they danced.

What a row! — and what a spectacle!

Red mud molded tightly over their scalps, fancy pigtails fore and aft, red and blue rings painted round their eyes — the red, ochrous mud; the blue by Reckitt. Native-made bells on hands and legs, cowtails, foxtails, leopard and lion skins, gaudy beads, miles of brassware, multi-colored shields, large shining spears, and wicked-looking clubs. All had their place in this wild dance.

Decked out with ostrich feathers, the principals, shouting, laughing, quivering, danced in a circle of their fellows, singing in honor of the King. They would shout a line, and the crowd would repeat a monotonous chorus, stamping out a rythm with the bells on their legs.

This is roughly how it went:

"Greetings to our King George;
He is a good King.

He lives in Europe with his wife;
He is a good King.
He has two daughters and many cows;
He is a good King.
He collects our poll tax every year;
He is a good King."

This goes on for hours — one tune, one rhythm, one chorus.

We were taken from group to group by Mazengo and his retinue of subchiefs and native police. Suddenly a wild-looking fellow dashed into the open, rushed at me, and held a razor-sharp spear within an inch of my midriff. He burst into a typical dance song, throwing himself about in various fearsome attitudes to illustrate his point. His song told of his illness, my treatment, the medicines drunk, sleep medicine, my little knife, and his subsequent recovery. At the end he threw his shield upon the ground at my feet, and shook me vigorously by the hand. For the moment I wondered who on earth he was, and then I suddenly realized he was my old friend, Sumu (literally, poison). I never really knew his real name, but I had called him that while he was a patient in our hospital. He had been brought in, a very sorry specimen, filled with aches and pains. I made a thorough investigation, taking drops of blood from his finger on dozens of occasions, looking for tropical fevers. I peered into his ear and down his throat, prodded him vigorously, and had him sitting up, saying: *Zingombe, zizi zose zili ziswanu,"* the African equivalent to "ninety-nine," but notwithstanding all my tests, I could find nothing. He got progressively worse. His legs were paralyzed, and then I noticed the unusual enthusiasm that his relatives had shown in giving him food. Day after day they brought him stew. It seemed a strange thing to me. One day Sumu shared his dinner with the patient next door, who immediately became violently ill. We suspected poisoning, and then it came out that Sumu had a great herd of cattle, and some of his relatives felt that they would rather that he was no more, so that his cattle should be theirs. They were poisoning him, giving him small doses, hoping thus to remove him quietly, and then they could share out, with due tribal ceremony, his big herd of humped-back cattle.

Guile had to be our watchword. I invited the chief to come over one day. His arrival coincided with that of the relatives, who had brought their usual big dish of stew. I told him of my suspicions, and whispered in his ear what I thought was an excellent idea. The old man looked at me for a moment, and then laughed till he cried. He held his sides and said:

"*Yo!* Bwana! what an idea! Will they not do everything to avoid it? And will I not insist with great strength? Indeed, we have them caught in a cleft stick."

And so the relatives were invited down to where the chief sat in state in a little grass hut, and a hospital dresser followed with the dish of stew. The great man sat solemnly and complimented them on their zeal in bringing such fine food for their sick relative. They squirmed uncomfortably, and then he said, severely:

"And now I want you to eat it."

"But how could we take the nourishing food of our dear relative?" said the older of the three.

The chief smiled. "Your zeal must have its reward," he said. And then, with a complete change of voice:

"Eat it, or be thrashed."

One of them made a clumsy effort to upset the dish, but the dresser forestalled him. I will never forget their looks as they ate that poisoned food. When they had finished, the chief said:

"Could you deceive the Bwana? Did he not know what you were doing? May you all be very ill! May you suffer as you deserve for your poisoning tricks!"

The chief walked away, chuckling as he saw the dresser giving each of the relatives a large tablespoonful of very powerful castor oil!

But Sumu looked very different now; he was the picture of physical health. I had massaged him for months, and taught him to do complicated physical exercises, and now here he was in front of me in fine fettle, waving his dangerous-looking spear. His little piece of byplay was greeted with great cheering by the assembly. By now the atmosphere was thick with the odor of sweating bodies and swirling clouds of blinding dust.

The chief gave an order to his clerk. We all went to a large clearing and sat on stools. To the huge listening crowd that pressed around us, Mazengo explained that King George was a Christian, and so, to end the day they would listen to the Word of God.

It thrilled me to hear the age old Gospel coming to these people, in their own tongue, preached by a clergyman of their own tribe. He took that old, old text that has meant so much to so many, John 3:16:

> "For God so loved the world, that He gave His only begotten Son, that whosoever believeth in Him should not perish, but have everlasting life."

As he pronounced the last words, the whole group bowed their heads in silence, and he prayed.

In the last light of the African day we sang "Rock of Ages" in Chigogo. The African clergyman prayed, lifting his hands in blessing towards his fellow tribesmen, wild-looking in their dance regalia, but now bowed quietly in prayer.

I thanked the chief for the afternoon's entertainment, and turned to go back to hospital, but hundreds thronged round to greet me. I recognized old patients. There was a feeling of friendliness about everybody that contrasted strangely with the experience of the pioneers. To me, that afternoon's happenings constituted one of the most powerful arguments in favor of the missionary cause which I could possibly conceive.

CHAPTER 8

At the Hospital

DRAMATIC surgery and wild drives through black seas of mud and swollen rivers have their own place in this job, but the most constructive work of all is done in the ordinary humdrum routine of hospital work.

The African loves routine. He calls it *taratibu,* and follows it more or less accurately; without it there is chaos. The day's work is listed, and every dresser and nurse has his or her special job and the time by which it must be done. Each day has its particular task: Monday, all cupboards are turned out; Tuesday, polishing of brassware and instruments; Wednesday, scrubbing walls; Thursday, debugging beds; Friday, making and sterilizing swabs and dressings.

The staff must be up with the sun, scrubbing floors, making beds, bathing patients, and giving early morning treatments. All must be finished by 8:30 a.m., when Yohanna, the gardener, bangs on an old flywheel. There is no loss of time for breakfast, as the Wagogo eat only twice a day, at noon and dusk, and at each meal it is *wugali* — porridge — with the appropriate relish.

Everyone turns up in uniform for staff prayers. A hymn is sung, most heartily and harmoniously. Then some verses are read from the Bible, and briefly explained by one or other of the Africans. They are masters of everyday stories to illustrate their points. Aesop seems to live again as they build a parable round some animal story. This particular morning one of the junior dressers read slowly and carefully from his Testament this verse:

> Neither is there salvation in any other, for there is none other Name under heaven given among men, whereby we must be saved.

He carefully put the Book down, paused a moment, then he spoke:

"I want you to understand that there is no other road to life but Jesus. Listen to my tale:

"Two monkeys were playing down by the swamp. One grasped a nut belonging to his fellow and threw it yards out into the soft mud. The other monkey bounded after it, and, landing in the middle of the quagmire, he began to sink. His struggles were futile. He kept on sinking, and when he was up to his middle, he called out to his friend: 'Help me, help me!'

"But the answer came back: 'Will I not get stuck, too? Pull yourself out!'

"The monkey that was stuck had a lovely pair of long whiskers. His companion said: 'Save yourself, monkey, pull yourself out by your whiskers. Heave, monkey, heave!'

"The monkey grabbed his whiskers, and pulled with all his might, but every moment he sank deeper. He was up to his neck, and he gave one tremendous, final heave to pull himself out of the mud that was engulfing him, but it was useless. A few minutes later a few bubbles, oozing slowly through the bog, was all that remained of the monkey, who thought he could save himself by his own efforts."

As he finished the story the dresser said, very simply:

"And the name of that bog was SIN.

"Remember, the only way out is by asking Jesus Christ, the Son of God, to save you from sin, and its consequences."

After some short and to the point prayers for the day's work, for our patients, and for our friends in Africa and overseas, the staff went off to their various jobs.

After I have given the orders for the day, the Sister and I go on our rounds of the wards:

(*In English*): "Daudi, three cataracts today at eleven o'clock. Premedication and cocaine, as usual."

"Yes, Bwana. Homatropin, too?"

I nodded.

(*In Chigogo*): "Bwana, the Sodi. Sulph. in the dispensary is finished. May I have the store key?"

"Righto, Samson. Here, catch!"

(*In Swahili*): "Did you do all yesterday's specimens Godwin?"

"Yes, Bwana."

"Let me have all yesterday's pathology reports, and repeat hemoglobin and worm examinations on Dina and Majimbi — Ward 2."

"Who is taking prayers with the outpatients today?"

"Yamusi and Mwendwa, Bwana."

Up comes Jonathan, a frowzy-looking specimen — he is the Mvumi Sewerage and Drainage Board.

"*Nghusaka miti ya choo* — Disinfectant, please."

"Go and ask Samson for it," said I, turning towards the wards.

"He says I waste it, and look here, Bwana, I've . . ." and he goes into unnecessary and lurid details about his work.

"Give me your hand," I command, and on his horny palm I write "disinfectant."

There were twelve cots on the maternity ward veranda, and all the mothers sat chatting in the sun, showing off their dusky-pink babies to admiring relatives and friends.

"How are the little ones?" I ask.

"All well, Bwana," comes the chorus.

"Their eyes, Mwendwa?"

"Only one a little red, I've followed the treatment *taratibu.*"

"Any temperatures?"

"Ndudula is 99.6°, but all the others are normal."

Old Sechelela had been up all night with two cases; these are the only ones in bed; yesterday's cases are out in the sun.

"Not very many this month, Sech!"

"Everyone is in their gardens these days, Bwana. Most of them have their babies at home and then go back to cultivate again."

"I suppose we'll have the same story about the bird scaring soon, when the harvest is ripening?"

"Oh, yes. Wagogo are hard people to help, especially when the *wadala* — old women — are busy with their tongues. Look at Ndebeto out there; she didn't have the baby on the way to the hospital. I went to look. No baby had been born where they showed me. Her people are very *shenzi* — heathen — and wanted special rites to be performed, so she had the baby in the house, and they have lied to you."

"What shall we do about it?"

"In our Chigogo custom, she should forfeit a goat."

"Right! I'll ask Pastor Mika to fix up the *shauri*."

Yuditi, the welfare teacher, came in then, and said, in English:

"May I begin the class for the mothers, sir?"

"Very well, Yuditi, what are you talking about today?"

"On the slogan: 'Milk only till the teeth come,' sir."

"Carry on, then."

Twenty mothers sat out in the sun, each with her baby on her back. They listen to all that is said, and repeat the slogans like kindergarten children. Their babies are weighed and examined, medicines given, and the women stroll home, talking volubly and clutching their babies' weight cards.

Across the way the nurse musters the general ward patients that are sitting in the sun, and hustles them into bed. I am shown the temperature book and various reports.

In the first bed is an old woman with advanced cataract, who has been prepared for operation. She came to us led by the hand. In a week she will be a very different person, able to walk out of hospital by herself and to see reasonably well.

The girl in the next bed is typical of many cases we see. For years her eyes have been untreated, and her lashes, by constantly sweeping her eye, have made deep ulcers. A little fancy surgical work and ophthalmic medication has corrected this.

In the corner beds are two women who are the derision of their fellows. They have been married for years, but have no children. Yesterday they were operated on, and should now have a fair chance of motherhood.

Lying propped up in another bed is a hollow-cheeked girl with advanced cancer. She is dying, and suffering intensely. She came to us too late for surgical aid, and we can only make her last days a little less trying. She is a Christian, and her faith is no empty confession.

"Bwana, read me that bit from St. John about God's House. It is more comforting than your little *sindano* — injection."

I read St. John 14 to her. That afternoon she passed on.

In the next ward were ten children.

"*Mbukwenyi, mbukwenyi* — Good morning, good morning" — yelled three convalescents, jumping up and down in their cots.

"I'm better, Bwana!"

"I want to go home!"

"And I!"

"And I, Bwana!"

Then a bit of rough and tumble, and the noisy ones are sent outside for a sunbath. A word with one, an entry on the papers of another. I examine a spleen here, and listen to a chest there.

I looked at the dressing of a little girl whose arm I had amputated. She had cancer of the bone. A month previously her father had come to me and said:

"Bwana, will you cut off her arm?"

"Why should I?"

"It smells so much that we cannot sleep with her in the house."

"But why did you not bring her in when it was little?"

"It did not smell then, Bwana, and besides, there were the gardens to cultivate."

"Did she not suffer pain?"

"Oh, yes, but if we had left the fields we should have had no food."

I looked hopelessly at the Sister. It was useless to talk to the father, but something had to be done about his daughter.

After three weeks of building up the child's physical condition, we operated. The little girl stood it well, but what the future may hold for her, one can only guess. Cancer is a foul disease.

A small laddie sitting up in bed had a mass of tuberculous neck glands as big as two closed fists.

"*Zugono,* Bwana? How did you sleep, sir?" said he, stretching out a trustful hand.

"*Zugono gwegwe wayiko, za singo?* — Same to you, old man. How's the neck?"

"*Ciba hadodo,* Bwana — a little better. And, Bwana" — in a very small voice — "I want to play in the sun."

I swept him up on my shoulder and walked on to the veranda, where I put him down beside a big red geranium, and gave him some old cotton reels to play with.

Daudi came running up. In his quaint English, he said:

"We has pneumonia boy, temp. 104 degrees and respiration 64, and two babies with the neck retracted."

"Admit 'em to Ward 2, Daudi, and call Othniel."

I went back to finish inspection, and in the bathroom found three dirty towels under a bucket. I was "reading the Riot Act" when Othniel appeared with his tray of slides, bottles and pathology apparatus.

"I want a report on those three children's blood slides as quickly as possible."

"Yes, sir," said he, and proceeded to prick fingers.

"*Wajenzi wafika,* Bwana — Visitors have arrived, sir," said a grinning boy at the door. This is the time-honored joke which means tea is ready.

Halfway through my second cup, I heard a very indignant "*Hodi*" at the door. The storeman had with him a guilty-looking washerman.

"Bwana, this man has burned a hole in a sheet because he was talking while he was ironing."

I saw the culprit and talked to him, long and forcibly. Samson gave me his monthly laundry report, which read:

LAUNDRY REPORT — MONTH AUGUST
Washed and ironed 1209 articules;
Used 52 inches of soap;
No losses or lacks;
One sheet holed out;
Required 16 new peggs, and repairs to one chimney.

I gulped down the remainder of my tea, and then visited outpatients.

Daudi was sitting at a table with attendance books before him.

"*Yunji* — Next, please," he called.

I walked in.

"Oh, sorry, sir," he said, standing up.

"All well here?" I asked.

"Yes, sir. Two eyes for you to see, and a baby with a big liver and spleen."

"Call them while I have a look at the dressings."

I arrived in the dressing room just in time to see the nurse drop a lump of ointment on the floor, scoop it up with her finger, and put it on an ulcer. Seeing me, she immediately broke into a wordy explanation: "Oh, Bwana, I only put the clean side of the ointment on the ulcer . . ."

Three women, having their chests rubbed, grinned, and a small girl, being liberally smeared with yellow sulphur ointment, said: "And she dropped my ointment, too!"

Next door, mothers held three struggling babies while a one-eyed nurse made repeated efforts to get brown drops into their eyes.

I walked back into the room where Daudi sat writing up treatment. Together we went to look at a small child.

"He has been ill for six months, Bwana. None of our medicine did any good, so we brought him to you," said the father, a tall Mugogo, with an ornate mud headdress.

The relatives crowded around as I examined his upper eyelids, which were turned inside out and were the color of an overripe cherry. He yelled and kicked, but I managed to see that his actual eyes were intact.

"Well," said the father, after a breathless hush, "what news?"

"The news is good," I replied. "I can fix up the eyes, but it means much work, and there will be several operations."

The relatives discussed the situation, then the father turned to me:

"We would want to stay as well, Bwana."

"I agree."

"*Ale nghani yimalika, assante,* Bwana! — The matter is settled, thank you, sir."

The men picked up sticks and spears, and the women adjusted the babies on their backs and walked in single file out of the hospital gate.

My other case was a youth with two scarred, sightless eyes, hopelessly ruined by a witch doctor, who had squeezed the juice of cactus into them. He had walked a hundred and twenty miles to get my help, but all I could tell him was that it was too late, the medicine man had produced a case beyond the help of any medical man.

People were patiently lined up outside the medicine bar, while a dresser took their tickets and measured out their particular brew. No patient is allowed to take medicine home. The chances are that first he would give his wife a dose, to make sure it wasn't poisonous. Should she survive, the whole family would get a taste, the baby getting an equal share with the rest, and then father would drink the entire dose at one time, to get better quickly. Our technique is to put each dose in half a pint of water, since the patient feels a long drink is much better and more satisfying than a mere spoonful.

As I went to make the rounds in the men's ward I heard an urgent voice behind me.

"Bwana, Bwana."

I ducked into my office, shut the door, and slipped out by another door into what I felt was the comparative peace of the men's compound. A man rose to his feet.

"Bwana, I want to sell you a . . ."

I made a beeline for the dispensary.

"Samson," I gasped, "these fellows are chasing me everywhere."

A face appeared at the window.

"Bwana, I want ——"

"Well, what do you want?" I replied.

There was no line of retreat from the dispensary.

"I want my wife to have the strong blue medicine that cured me. That medicine's the stuff. *O-o-o-o-o-o,* it's good!"

I left Samson to explain to him that his wife wanted the thick white medicine because she was not suffering from rheumatism as he had been, but from indigestion!

Standing beside the ward door was a subchief. He had his mouth open, and was making queer sounds that seemed to point to intense agony. As I peered at his teeth, I heard a clamor of voices behind me. There was a man trying to sell a roll of rope; another wanted to explain that it was time his wife went home, because he was getting tired of doing his own cooking. Still another came complaining that thc washerman had tied up one of his goats, which, it appeared, had been taking undue interest in some of the hospital sheets! They all tried to speak at once, emphasizing their own particular needs, with elaborate pantomime. It was the nearest thing to Babel I have ever heard. I had

had three hours' sleep the night before, due to the arrival of three babies. Two very exacting operations had to be performed, and there were still sixty sick people to see, and routine treatment to be ordered for a group of lepers. I felt hopeless, and turned to the jabbering, struggling mass of humanity, and said in English — which, of course, they couldn't understand: "Stone the crows, you chaps, I wish you'd shut up, any more of that racket and I'll fly right off the handle."

There was a chuckle from behind me, and I saw Daudi.

"Bwana," he said, "shall I translate that into Chigogo for you?"

"Please, Daudi. But you must do it accurately!"

He laughed, and coming close, whispered: "Say to them, *Nghusaka kumeza, mate.*"

"What?" I said. "*Nghusaka* means 'I want'. *Kumeza* — 'to swallow' — *mate* — 'spit'. Surely, Daudi, that's wrong?"

"No, Bwana, that's right. You try it, and see!"

"If you're having a game with me, Daudi, I will give you the job of making zinc ointment until your shoulders ache."

Daudi smiled. "Try it, Bwana. See if it's a joke."

So I went to the door. Half a dozen hands reached out to clutch me.

"*Anye,*" I cried. "*Nghusaka kumeza mate.*"

For a second there was silence, and then a roar of laughter.

"*Yah,*" they said. "*H-e-e-e-e,* behold, he knows," and chuckling, they went to sit in the shade and wait till I had finished my medical work. I turned to Daudi.

"*Yah!* It worked all right!"

"Yes, Bwana, it is our custom. Follow our custom, think our thoughts, speak our language, and then you will help our people."

The Little Ones

WELFARE BABIES

Living proof of the possibilities of healthy African childlife are these two husky and jolly youngsters born at the hospital.

". . . I took ten children of the hospital helpers and sent out to the village to get ten children of the same age . . . The children who had been looked after according to the principles of mothercraft were stronger, healthier and more cheerful-looking than those who had been brought up by native methods. . . . I called the girls together and showed them the difference, and said: "What is the reason?" They answered in chorus: "Breast feed is best feed, and nothing but milk till the teeth appear."

(Babies)

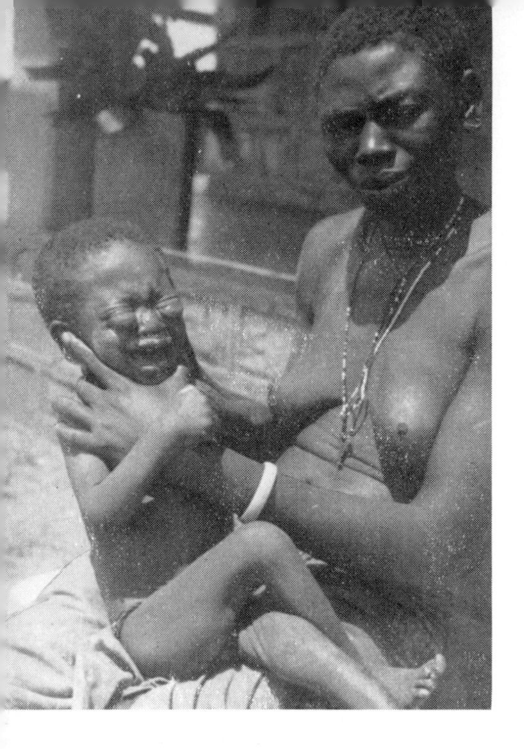

WITCH DOCTOR'S HANDIWORK

The horribly blinded eyes of this little child are the result of a witch doctor's "cure." The child originally suffered from trachoma, which is common.

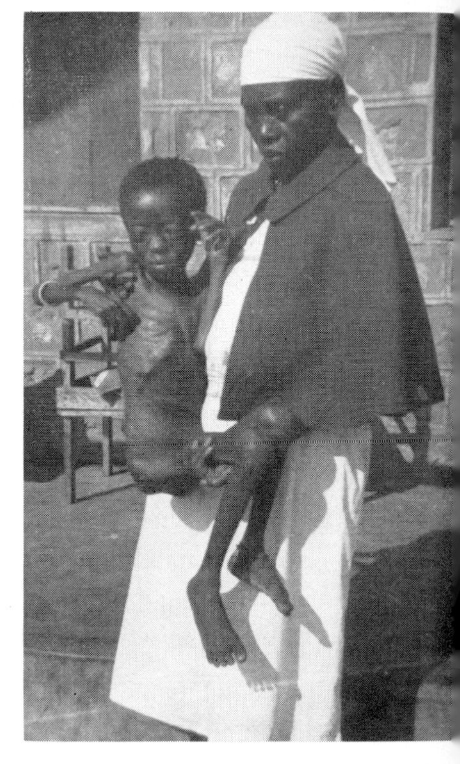

A child with rickets, in old Sechelela's arms, shows what all too often occurs as a result of improper diet and care.

A typical case of cancer

Carefully I wrote this new gem of African speech in a little notebook and got on with the day's work. Yamusi was finishing the preparation of a young man's leg for operation. He had contracted a fungus disease, and the whole of his foot now needed special treatment under an anesthetic. He was terrified at the thought of the anesthetic. He gripped my hand.

"Bwana, I am frightened. This *nusu caputi* — literally 'half dead' — terrifies me. Surely I will die. Oh, *Yaya gwe.*"

"Sila, there's nothing to fear. Four times have I breathed this medicine myself when doctors in my own country removed sundry portions of me that were not required, and, behold, am I dead?"

"No, Bwana, but then you are not I."

Yamusi took a turn in the conversation.

"Listen, Sila. I had your trouble. I breathed the sleep medicine no less than ten times. My relatives said I would die, but the Bwana, with the help of God whom we serve in this hospital, cured me. I, too, was frightened. So I prayed, and asked that the peace of God might rule in my heart, and behold, am I not now 'Ward Sister'?"

We moved on to the next bed whose occupant was an old, wrinkled man, from a tribe a hundred and eighty miles away. I was struck by the fact that he seemed to take everything that happened as his right, never saying "thank you," and now that he was ready to go home he did not appear in the least grateful, although undoubtedly we had saved his life, and the doing of it had been a far from savory task. Yamusi whispered to me:

"He does not belong to our tribe, Bwana, and he is hard to understand. I want, however, to make him say he is grateful."

He turned to the old man. "Well, father. You are better now."

"*E-e-eh-u-g-h,*" came from the bed. "Yes, I am better. The charm round my neck made that happen."

Yamusi was a little taken aback. "*Kah!* and what about all the medicine that you have drunk?"

"The charm in the piece of string that I wear round my middle makes the medicine work."

"*Kah,*" said Daudi in disgust. "And what about the kindness of the Bwana, and of the nurses, and of the dressers?"

"*A-a-a-a-h,*" said the old man, cunningly, "that's the charm that I wear round my left ankle that makes people kind to me."

Daudi snorted. "Yamusi, next time any of this tribe come into the hospital, do not shave off their hair, but cut off all the charms. *Kah!* Charms! that make people kind to him!"

Yamusi was smiling, but he was not angry.

"Listen, father. Bits of string and crushed beetles rubbed on to them, and other bits of string with calf skin and bits of dried chicken's inside can never, never help you to know *Mulungu umulungulungu* — the God of Gods. There is only one way of being fit to come face to face with Him after your body has died and your spirit passes on, and that way is by asking His Son, Jesus Christ, who was nailed to a tree by wicked men, to come in and cleanse your heart. He died to pay the price of the evil that would keep you from seeing God face to face. No charm can do this."

The old man shook his head. "No, I have a charm on my right ankle that helps me in these matters."

Sila, the operation case, whom I had just seen, turned to him.

"Father, when you feel your life is in danger as I do, a little charm is no comfort, but a living God is a very real one."

Othniel came up with his report — the pneumonia child actually had tick fever; the other had a severe malarial infection, while the neck retraction cases had no parasites at all.

"Set up two trays, one for routine injections, and the other for lumbar puncture."

Yamusi was standing patiently before an open cupboard.

"I've got fourteen patients and twelve beds, Bwana! I want more blankets, more sheets, and a bucket of bandages."

I gave him a note for these, and then saw the patients.

"Bwana," said Yamusi, "we're terribly short of pajamas. Things are so bad that I give those who can walk about the trousers, and those that must stay in bed have the coats."

He took me from bed to bed, telling me the temperatures, pulses and new symptoms of each patient.

There was Rajabu, a Moslem, with osteoarthritis. His knees had to be massaged daily.

The eye tray was brought to me, and, sitting on a chair with the patient on a stool in front of me, I instilled drops of cocaine to minimize pain.

A corneal ulcer is an ulcer actually on the eye. Untreated, it spreads, and often perforates the eye, blinding it. In five minutes I had dealt with three of these, at a cost of twopence each, and saved three persons' eyesight.

A nurse came to the door.

"Bwana, Bibi wants you to see a newborn baby. There is trouble with its mouth."

In the nursery I found a baby girl who was tongue-tied. Knowing that that would inevitably lead to complications, I made facetious remarks to the Sister, and proceeded to do the necessary minor operation. Sechelela walked in as I was drying my hands.

"Sechelela," said the Sister, "the Bwana has been saying that he has saved this child from explosion."

The old African woman looked at the child critically, pulled up her night-gown, and carefully inspected her anatomy.

"Exploding! The child looks quite well."

I made for the door. "It's a girl, Sech, of your own family, and it was tongue-tied!"

I didn't wait for a post mortem on these remarks!

The next hour was spent in doing one of the most disgusting operations that tropical medicine offers. Samson had tied a towel round his face as well as his mask. Daudi and I operated.

"*Kah!*" said Daudi. "Sila may object to having an anesthetic, but, *kah!* he is fortunate that he is the patient, and not the surgeon."

I nodded assent, putting an iodoform dressing over the great area that I had cleaned up. Yamusi came to the door that we used to take patients to and from the ward.

"Yamusi, put an iodoform dressing on this once every day. Use a shield to keep the clothes from touching the foot, and give him aspirin for his pain."

"Bwana, I can do some of that treatment, but there is no iodoform left."

"*Yah,*" said Daudi, "we are always short of something."

I knew just how unsavory the ward would be unless that foot was dressed with a medicine that covered the terrible smell.

"I will think about it, Yamusi. We will find something else——"

And next morning we put on a dressing of crushed sterilized charcoal. It was certainly not the best form of treatment, but it was a link in the chain of the recovery of young Sila. As I adjusted it, I asked:

"Well, Sila, what of the anesthetic?"

He smiled. "It smells badly, Bwana. *Yah!* But behold, it takes away the pain. Behold, I was greatly helped by God yesterday."

"You will be fit, Sila, to come to church on Sunday. The dressers will carry you, bed and all, and put you down in the back of the church."

"*Kah,*" said Daudi. "The Bwana's going to preach on Sunday. I wonder what he will say?"

I smiled. "Daudi, I've prepared this sermon carefully. I have practised it over and over again, and even tried it on the cook. I have written it out in English, and Chigogo. It's simple and direct, but I'd like you to take a piece of paper, and write down any corrections that you think should be made."

Daudi nodded.

I moved into the pulpit on the Sunday morning, and watched three hundred Africans singing the last verse of "Fight the good fight." There was Yuditi, our welfare worker, playing the organ. Daudi was in the choir, singing a very powerful bass. Yamusi was arranging his patient's pillows. The schoolgirls in the front seats were obviously wondering what I was going to say. Through the whitewashed doorway I could see shimmering heat waves, and a mirage over the plain. Some black and white crows cawed raucously in a nearby baobab tree. The whole congregation bowed in prayer. I was tremendously impressed with the way they listened. They seemed to hang on every word. Just as I was concluding my talk, I saw Sechelela hurrying down from the hospital. She beckoned urgently to me. I rounded off my remarks and hurried after her. It was just another of the eight hundred babies that arrive each year, but one that would have been lost, but for my help. I put on my coat, and went to the door. Outside was Daudi in his Sunday best, a piece of paper in his hand.

"Well, Daudi, how did it go?"

"*Swanu,* Bwana, good. Here are your corrections." He pushed the paper into my hand, and then disappeared at the double. This was most unusual. Fearing the worst, I read his remarks:

Dear Bwana

It seems strange to me that there should be five wise kettles, and five foolish ones. Do kettles get married, or is it perhaps that you forgot that *birika* is a "kettle," while a "maiden" is *bikira?*

I went back into the ward. "Sechelela, I have just preached a sermon on the ten kettles."

The old lady looked at me solemnly. "And who was it, Bwana, who was speaking of the tongues of womankind?"

I withdrew from the ward, feeling, this time, that the laugh was definitely on me!

The first Monday afternoon of the month was specially set aside, obstetrics permitting, for making up my monthly report. I sat in my 8x10 foot mud-brick office, hard at it. Two thousand four hundred and sixty-two outpatients seen; thirty cataracts done; twenty-eight of them had gone home under their own steam, full of the praises of the hospital. They could see again after years of blindness.

The welfare worker came to the door.

"Filling in the report, Bwana?"

"Yes, Yuditi."

"I've had six hundred women coming for advice during the month. I should say we have saved at least fifty babies from certain death by giving the mothers simple advice and not even a teaspoonful of medicine!"

The microscope expert popped his head through the window.

"Two hundred and four specimens examined, Bwana."

"Good," I said. "We've got the fever difficulty by the tail now."

The African lad laughed.

"Even when you're away on safari we know just what to do when we find the germs in the blood. Then, with the routine treatment book, we can follow the whole matter through, give the right medicine in the right dose, and save lives and lives and lives."

I wrote the figures down in the report and smiled at the Sister, who had pioneered in the hospital and done the bigger part of the job.

"It's the routine work that counts, Sister, and it's training the Africans to do it themselves. That's the very heart of this job of ours."

CHAPTER 9

Kongwa — Berega

THERE had been feverish activity in the dispensary for a week, preparing and packing drugs. We had eight kerosene tins of various ointments and six of castor oil, barrels of concentrated cough mixture, a keg of liniment, and three quarters of a ton of Epsom salts. In large tins were thousands of pills — 80,000 aspirin, 30,000 cascara, 40,000 quinine, and 50,000 soda mints. Each tin had a cup attached to measure out the pills by the five hundred. There were syringes, needles and medicines enough for 35,000 injections, twenty-five gallons of other assorted medicines, and a heap of cotton blankets and sheets, which we had bought at bargain prices from an Indian patient.

To pack the car with tins, casks, kegs, bottles, bandages, boxes of soap and bedding seemed a hopeless task, but at last we got away on our two hundred mile journey over mountain and plain to Berega, our outpost C.M.S. Hospital in the Uluguru mountains, some one hundred miles inland from the shores of the Indian Ocean.

The first lap took us over a stretch of typical Ugogo. It was an amazingly full cross-section of Gogo life. In front of flat-roofed squat houses, with gardens of sorghum and maize, women sat pounding and grinding. There was a man driving a cow before him, a rope of baobab fibre tied to the animal's hind leg. Little naked boys looked after groups of lean, humpbacked cattle. Nakedness is no cause for shame to the boys of this tribe until the circumcision rites are performed, after which they wear a loincloth, and would not think of appearing without it. The flats shimmered in the burning, direct rays of the sun. The cook's understudy solemnly counted seventy-eight occasions on which I changed into low gear to nose our way carefully through dry river beds or thornbush, flanked by erosion channels.

Handali is the name given to a collection of mud-brick *dukas,* where Indian traders sell cloths, blankets, kerosene by the pint, flashlight batteries, onions, hoe heads, wire ornaments, blue mottled soap, and the thousand and one things dear to a native's heart.

Abadou, as the Africans called him, or Abdul Kassam Visram, commission agent and general merchant, to quote from his letterhead, came to his door to greet me. Behind him stood his little wife, Fatima, with her long plait of jet black hair.

Fatima maintains that I have twice saved her life. Moreover, she knows my taste in tea, and rushed off to boil a kettle, while I went past the little mosque to see Suliman, her brother, and one of the hospital's staunchest friends.

We crossed the railway near the straggly little town of Kikombo. Translated literally the name means "Little Hole," and the town does nothing to belie it. Gruesome stories are told by the missionaries who were interned here during the 1914-18 war. One night everybody was herded into the corrugated iron freight shed at Kikombo Station. Their shoes were taken from them as a precaution against escape — no one could walk more than ten yards without them in this thorn country. Occasionally the sentry drove his bayonet through the wall to emphasize his presence. Men and women, many ill with dysentery, and, for the most part, half starved, were cooped together in this airless African version of the Black Hole.

As I drove past the huddled group of corrugated iron shanties arranged round the town market place, a fat Hindu in a purple shirt worn outside a baggy pair of trousers, stopped me:

"Sir, will you do me the great honor of examining my lungs with stethoscope?"

I pulled up, and room was made for me to sit in state among the litter of merchandise on the mud floor. He insisted on being examined in the front of his shop. Off came his shirt, and he sat in adipose state in full view of the passersby. Every movement I made was greeted with deep admiration by a group of Africans in the background and his family, who occupied the dress circle.

At last, having escaped the horror of drinking warm, spiced milk with some unidentified green things floating in it, I drove to our first stop at Buigiri Hospital.

Here we reduced our load somewhat. Samson, the dispenser, filled all the stock bottles, scooped out thousands of pills, and groaned as he tried to put unwilling ointments into narrow-necked bottles. Soon he was smeared liberally with paregoric, oil of cloves, methylene blue, and castor oil. In the meantime, I was diagnosing some eye cases, seeing the inpatients, and admiring the babies, to the immense joy of their mothers.

We had still fifty miles to go to reach Kongwa by nightfall. As the sun was setting red over the mountains, we waved farewell to the staff. The road wound in and out of forest and hill country, thick thornbush was everywhere. A bevy of guinea-fowl scuttled across the road, flying off into the trees. It was growing dark as behind us lay the warm glow of a beautiful sunset, and ahead the black masses of the hills.

To reach Kongwa, we had to turn off into dense bush, and we were thankful for the light as the full moon rose majestically over Kongwa Mountain. This mountain is said to be haunted, and no local tribesman would climb it at night for any price.

We had to steer directly into the moon, as there was no sign of any road. Without the headlamps, we made our way slowly through the marvellous night. The baobabs loomed up, sinister in the silent forest, and a hyena stopped in its slinking run to look curiously at us. I switched on the lights to descend steeply into the gloom of a river bed, and, as we came from its darkness into silver moonlight again, we saw Kongwa before us. There was the rhythmic "tonka! tonk!" of the drums and the howl of a jackal as we passed through the village to the hospital.

The mission house is a wide, two-storied building. I felt intensely alone in this great empty place as the wind swept dismally over the plains and shrieked around the house. As I walked on the wide balcony, a bat brushed past my head. The hills stood out clearly against the white vastness of the plain, and from the distant mountain came the roar of a lion. An owl hooted in the thornbush nearby. From the village came again the fitful rhythm of the drums.

At two in the morning a drunken wretch came and serenaded me on the front doorstep. I threw half a bucket of water in his direction. With a yell, he leaped off through the thornbush. I have often wondered what story he told his cronies; it would certainly be embellished by spirits and devils that spat at him!

Something in that house always gave me asthma, so I sat, wrapped in a blanket, in a deck chair. Before dawn I fell into a disturbed sleep, dreaming that I was being choked, and woke with a start to find my car boy, Roger, standing beside me with a cup of tea — and the news that we had eight punctures.

The road east from Kongwa (which, incidentally, is the main road from the Coast to the Lakes) is a narrow, rough track cut about mercilessly for scores of miles by the storm water that rushes down from the Kiboriani Range, which towers above it.

Moving very carefully over the scarcely defined track, deep-furrowed by the cattle, we came to the market. Here there seemed to be hundreds of women waiting for water. A pipeline from a spring in the hills leads down to a tap, and an important-looking Swahili, in red fez and immaculate *kanzu,* presides over the supply. The women did not queue up, but placed their guords, calabashes, pots and tins in line, and went off to sit in the shade and gossip.

For fifteen miles we were passing women walking to the water pipe; some of them spend all their time walking to and from the market, their water supply skilfully balanced on their heads. With their babies on their backs, these women walk most gracefully, and their poise and physique are a pleasure to see.

I was driving along in a reverie when the car boy suddenly said, in a high pitched voice:

"*Ulanje*, Bwana, *Nzila akulya* — Look, sir, the road is right over there!"

I started so violently that we skidded half off the road, and, with difficulty, I righted the car.

"What did you do that for? *Kah!* your voice was so squeaky I nearly jumped out of my skin."

The African regarded me gravely. "Bwana, when we want to show a thing is very far away, then we use a high pitched voice; see, is not the road far away?"

There it lay before us, a long, red ribbon winding away into the dimness of the plain. We dared not go fast, as there had been a shower of rain, and every now and then a soil erosion gash a foot wide would appear immediately in front of the wheels.

Great granite crags hundreds of feet high loomed above us. We passed Gogo *kayas* almost hidden in the standing corn, and small boys herding cattle by the roadside. A herd of gazelle trotted off into the bush as we approached. I stopped just over the provincial boundary at Mulali, a native town well watered and shaded by hundreds of tall umbrella trees. Great hornbills cried dismally overhead. The trees were a mass of weaver birds' nests, and the industrious little yellow fellows were chattering noisily about their homes.

The villagers thronged around us. Here, on the border of Ugogo, I found that some were able to speak Chigogo, while others speak Kimegi. Fortunately, I knew just enough of this latter dialect to greet them. For the most part, the people seem to think that Europeans know only

Swahili. They advance and say "*Jambo,* Bwana," which is the usual Swahili utility salutation. If you reply in their own dialect, they break into broad smiles and are tremendously pleased.

This is how it sounded. Up came Suliman, the native clergyman:

"*Mbukewa,* Bwana Doktari," said he.

"*Mbukwa,* Pastor," I replied in Chigogo.

An old man with white, closely curled hair and a little scraggy beard, walked gravely forward and said, in Kimegi:

"*Bahogonile.*"

"*Hanoga, bahonagwe,*" I replied, and solemnly shook hands — a ritual comprising first grasping the fingers, then the thumb, and then the fingers again.

A Masai with a red-ochred pigtail and a cruel-looking knife, passed by, driving two cows.

"*Sobai,*" said he.

"*Ebba,*" I replied.

The sum total of all these greetings was the conventional "Good morning." Not to greet an African is a deadly insult, while to do it efficiently is a sure way of gaining his friendship.

While at Mulai I saw, and treated, half a dozen eye cases, after which we moved off, to a chorus of farewells in four different languages.

The country began to change perceptibly. We climbed and turned through thick, tall forests, sometimes dropping sharply to cross a mountain stream, and then, in low gear, crawling up what seemed to be one-in-five slopes.

It had been raining, and these red hills were as slippery as buttered glass. We put chains on the wheels, and at the rear tied a great piece of timber which fell into place behind the wheels when we skidded towards the deep ditches on both sides of the road.

Great rock masses, sheer-faced, stood out from the road. One of these, called *Nhembo* — elephant — by the locals, has a wierd reputation. They say after a mist it can often be seen for miles, lighted up by sheets of bluish flame. Many Europeans vouch for this fact, too. I had inspected the spot carefully but could detect nothing unusual.

At long last the thatched roofs of Berega came into view through the tall grass. We swung into a beautiful garden where the air was fragrant with the scent from an avenue of frangipanni.

There was the village. Round, conical-roofed huts, the school, the church, the hospital, and above all towered the great hill, Chimhinda, to which the villagers' ancestors fled from marauding Masai and waged guerilla warfare from its heights.

Again there was the usual round of measuring pills, filling jars of ointment, checking lists, repair of instruments and talking to the staff about their responsibilities. A cataract was done on the dispensary table, and a night was spent in trying to deal with one of the most ghastly obstetric emergencies.

The Wakaguru are a tribe steeped in superstition. A living thorn fence had to be grown round the maternity ward to keep away witches, before the women would come to the hospital. A visitor once caught an owl, and was viewed with tremendous suspicion by the people, who regarded her as a dabbler in the worst variety of magic.

It has taken years of patient work to gain the confidence of the people. Prejudices had to be broken down, but as they saw the effectiveness of the treatment given, and, occasionally, dramatic recovery when they had given up all hope, they grew to trust us.

From medical standards, the hospital is hopelessly inadequate, understaffed, and under-equipped. One European Sister and some six Africans comprise the staff. They work in mud-walled, grass-thatched buildings, whose only claim to luxury is a concrete floor. With the simplest of medicines and supplies, a solid, progressive work, out of all proportion to the cost, is being done. For instance, in a recent meningitis epidemic, twenty-five lives were saved at a cost of ten shillings per life.

By medical missionary effort, we are saving lives, relieving suffering, and all the time building up confidence. At the same time we are training Africans of character to take the place of the village witch doctor.

A favorite expression on safari in Tanganyika is "crack-a-dawn," a time variously interpreted. The sun was hardly up when we moved homeward. Some miles out we were met by three Masai who wanted a lift. In every way these fierce nomad tribesmen, who have wandered down from the Nile basin, are unlike the Bantu people of East Africa.

They are tall and slender, and go in for the most amazing bead and brasswork ornaments. Their cattle are their life. Where there is grass and water, there they stay, moving on to better grazing country when the fodder is finished. They never wash themselves, but rub their bodies with rancid butter and red ochre — an effect not pleasing either to the eye or to the nose. Their food is blood and milk. An animal's vein is neatly nicked, and, after a pint of blood is collected, the wound is then staunched with cow dung.

The Masai hut is only about three feet high, and is made of bent saplings. Over a wicker framework is plastered mud and cow dung. Into this the whole family crawls at night.

Our three passengers traveled with us for ten miles, and then invited us to their village, which was quite near the road. A number of huts and a big thorn *boma* for the cattle was all that it boasted, except for millions of flies, which crawled into your eyes and had to be forcibly wiped away.

The women, their forearms and legs hidden under massive spirals of brassware, and with the same ornament around their necks, had the appearance of having their heads stuck through a life belt. On their backs were beautifully decorated gourds of sour milk.

We said "*Sobai*" to the men, but — as it is not polite to greet a woman in this way — we said "*Ndagwenya*" to them, which means exactly the same thing.

One of them told us that they had recently moved the village because of a calamity in their midst. A man had died a seemingly natural death, and, following their burial customs, his body had been tied to a tree and left. The first night the hyenas had not touched it, and everyone was most concerned. The second night they heard the howling of the scavengers, but again the body was untouched. On the third night the forest was silent, and when the anxious elders went early to look they found the corpse as it had been placed originally. They brought the news back to the village, which, without delay, moved into another part of the country.

The highlight of that day's safari was when we saw a man luxuriating in a pool of storm water in the middle of the road. Coasting silently up to within a few yards of him, I blew the horn. He rose straight into the air, and hardly seemed to touch ground as his black figure disappeared into the bush.

Those in the car laughed till they cried, and regarded it as the joke of the year.

CHAPTER 10

Witchcraft and Native Medicine

THINGS are seldom monotonous in a Mission Hospital in Tanganyika. Nearly always there is something happening at Mvumi. But, for once, things were unaccountably slack. By eleven a.m. I had done a round of the wards and had seen the outpatients, the dispenser was turning out medicines at a great rate, an African teacher was giving a class of nurses a lecture on digestion, and, apart from thirty babies on the veranda, the maternity ward was quiet. I went into the laboratory, to find the microscope in its case, and the head dresser polishing some slides with the remnants of an old shirt.

"Things quiet here, Daudi?"

"They are today, Bwana, and about time, too. Let us go together to the village at the foot of the hill Cikanga. The chief there has been singing your praises because you saved his wife's life when you operated to take away that tumor she had."

"*Viswanu* — all right," I said, "we'll go straight after lunch."

It was blazing hot. Our path led us over sandy river beds, through clumps of cactus, tangles of thornbush and between great granite boulders. Tucked away behind a conical-shaped hill was Nzije's village.

We called "*Hodi*" at the headman's house. A toothless old woman was on the roof making a food bin, molding it, rung by rung, from red mud and cow dung. She saw us, and pointed south with pursed lips. "He is right over there," said she, in a high-pitched voice. Turning in this direction, we came to a place where ten men were building a new house.

I was amused to see that the great wickerwork grain baskets, which hold nearly a ton of grain, were first placed in line, and then the house built around them. Ticks and vermin become so bad that, after five years, the house has to be pulled down. The family lives in a cornstalk shanty until the new *kaya* — native house — is built.

Further on we came to women brewing beer. They had reached the stage of pounding the sprouting seed, preparatory to brewing in great six gallon clay pots.

At last we found Nzije watching a man mixing mud with water and crude castor oil for a headdress. With him was an old man with great, pendulous ear lobes and a wealth of ornaments.

I greeted everyone with the greatest ceremony. The chief invited me to come to his house and to tell them of our words. By this he meant to tell them about Jesus Christ. Daudi whispered to me:

"The old man with the hardware in his ears is a witch doctor, Bwana. He doesn't like your being here. Let us talk of magic, and then you show some of your tricks." (One of my schoolboy hobbies had been conjuring.)

"Go very quietly, Bwana, and leave the talking to me first."

At the chief's place stools were brought for us, and we sat under a thorn tree. Soon over a hundred people were there. The men sat on logs and poles, the small boys on pumpkins, while the women were in the background squatting on their haunches, or sitting on the ground feeding their babies.

Goats and calves walked about everywhere, fondled by the children, and ignored by the adults.

Nzije had been drinking native beer, and was very talkative.

"We Wagogo can do fine work," said he, pointing with his chin to a grain bin he was making.

I agreed.

"We know many things that the *Wazungu* — Europeans — don't."

Again I nodded.

Then an old man spoke up.

"None of our *Waganga* — witch doctors — could do what the Bwana did for me. You all remember me as a blind man — blind for years. I could do nothing. Often I fell down holes, or walked into the fire, or scratched myself on thornbush. One day the Bwana here saw me at the hospital. He gave me medicine to take away my pain, and then, with his little knife, he took away my *vipece.* Here they are."

He shook from a little wooden bottle two dried-up eye-lenses that looked like split peas. Everyone crowded round to have a look.

"Did he cut your eye?" said the chief, fingering the specimens. "Did it not hurt you?"

"He cut my eye, truly, but the medicine he put in first took away the pain. I lay in bed for days with my eyes bandaged, and then, one day, he unwound the bandage, and, *Yah!* I could see. No witch doctor has ever done that."

There was a sudden hush. Covert glances were cast at the witch doctor. Nobody said a word.

"Tell me," I said to the chief, "can your *Waganga* really do great miracles, or do they just strut about like the cock who crows, but cannot lay eggs?"

Everyone laughed and started to talk. The chief was silent. The witch doctor looked utterly disinterested.

"Tell me," I went on, in Chigogo Chetu — Gogo custom — "what would you give a *Muganga* who could push an egg through a clay cooking pot and break neither the egg nor the pot?"

There was an immediate roar of laughter at the utter absurdity of the idea.

The chief consulted with the old men. They muttered together, and then he answered, after due deliberation:

"A cow, a fat one."

"Then bring me a pot and an egg."

Nzije's wife shuffled off to get them; everyone was agog.

"Hold this pot, father" (this to a white-headed ancient), "and tell everyone if there are eggs inside or not."

He peered inside, and announced, "No eggs, Bwana, not even a little one."

I took the egg, palmed it, and made elaborate efforts to push it through the baked clay. They watched breathlessly, and a gasp of "*Kah!*" came from everyone when they saw the egg appear intact in my hand inside the pot.

No one spoke. Some of the more timorous got to their feet furtively and prepared for immediate flight. The ancient looked into the pot, and the chief held the egg at arm's length.

"*Kah!*" said he, "that's magic — greater than anything I've seen."

He called his son. "Maswaga, bring Bwana the brindle cow."

I stopped him short, and said: "No, *Muwaha* — great one — I do not want your cow; I haven't come to take your riches, but to show you the truth. I have nothing to hide, that was not magic; I simply deceived your eyes by the quickness of my hand."

"But we saw you do it, you *did* do it!" cried the ancient.

Without comment, I demonstrated the trick without the clay pot.

Amazed exclamations from all sides, and then they laughed.

Up jumped a hospital dresser, and, in very simple language, told them of Jesus Christ, how He came to bring us light, light from God; how He had come to deal radically with sin. He compared it to the old man's cataracts:

"When they were in his eyes, he was blind and useless. He could see nothing; he hurt himself and was a burden to others, but when his darkened lenses were gone, he could see."

The old man got to his feet again.

"These are not just idle words," he cried, "they are real. I *can* see! And it is also true about Jesus Christ. I learned of Him, too, when I was in hospital. Once I feared death, and now I do not, because I know that Jesus is God and that He has taken away the obstruction that stopped me from seeing God."

The dresser drove home his point. "He came, not only to patch up the body, which must die some time, but to tell how the soul can be healed."

They listened with rapt attention for nearly an hour. When we got up to go, the chief firmly gripped my hand:

"You will come again soon, Bwana; these are weighty words."

Next day the witch doctor turned up at the hospital. He told Samson he wanted to see me. Very confidentially, he whispered that he would give me three cows (a princely sum) if I would teach him to do that wonderful deceiving trick.

Much of the witch doctor's work is sheer fraud, but over and over they produce cures because they produce a tangible cause for the trouble.

I once saw a girl with cow's horns attached by suction to her head. She had had headaches, and was on a visit to the local *Muganga*. He had received his digging fee and gone off to the forest for roots and herbs. These he had cooked with elaborate ceremony, and, of course, had ordered a goat to be killed for its fat. She had swallowed a gourd full of this brew, and promptly vomited. Being an opportunist, the *Muganga* turned to the relatives and said:

"There, look! The poisons come away at once."

To get rid of those actually affecting the head, he had put on the horns, which, on removal, contained pebbles, dirt and fragments of bone. These he triumphantly displayed as the cause of all the trouble, and, secure in the knowledge that no one would think of looking in those horns before they were put on, he walked home the richer by a cow.

Undoubtedly, they have some useful medicines, notably bark extracts for diarrhea, that act like orthodox medicines; also, for gastritis, they give a crude variety of alkaline powder, but there is no idea of dosage, and scores of people die from drinking pints of otherwise helpful, though mildly poisonous, concoction. The fact that they vomit saves many.

Wherever the Africans have a pain local treatment is applied. The *Muganga* takes a knife and scratches deeply into the skin. You find folk with hundreds of these scratches covering their abdomens and legs. This is a very crude substitute for antiphlogistine, or the mustard plaster, and, since cow dung is often rubbed in, it is not free from complications. One woman came to us literally covered with great raised keloid scars, all arising from these scratches. These scars, several inches long, and raised high from the skin surface, look like mountains on a huge relief map. Once they are there, nothing can be done. Remove them and they return bigger and less treatable. A few pennyworth of liniment and a handful of aspirin tablets would have cured this particular woman. As a matter of fact, they did, but not before native treatment had left its ineradicable mark.

There are those who do not claim to be a *Muganga,* but are specialists in one line. They collect a fee of a dish of corn, or a chicken, for their labors. In particular, these people treat the throat, or, as they call it, "*Kutula Malaka,*" literally, "to break the throat."

My first experience of this was to see a two year old baby who had a cough. I had treated him, and he was progressing nicely. One evening he was brought in dying, his lips blue and his eyes staring. His throat was a great angry red, inflamed mass, and he couldn't breathe. I rushed for instruments to make an opening into his windpipe and give him a chance to breathe. It was too late; he was dead before I could even light a hurricane lantern.

The parents said: "Oh, it just happened by itself in the morning." I was utterly at sea, having never seen nor heard of anything like it before. But old Sechelela explained that it was a case of *"Kutula Malaka"*; the operator had first dipped her fingers into urine and then scraped the back of the throat, to remove "the teeth there which caused all the trouble."

"Probably, Bwana, old Suzannah did it; she is a *fundi* — an expert," said Sechelela.

Two days later Suzannah came to the hospital. She was old and bent with rhuematism; her hands were like talons and her nails long and unspeakably dirty. In a whining voice she told me a story of pains in her joints and her back. I was about to prescribe when I saw Sechelela beckoning me at the door. I went up to her:

"What's up?" I asked.

She laughed cunningly. "Do you want to see some fun, Bwana?"

"Surely, but what do you want me to do?"

"Tell Suzannah you must *tula* her *malaka,* and see what happens."

She was hardly able to control her mirth when I went back and asked the old woman about her head and neck and ears. All had a long tale associated with them.

Then I said: "Open your mouth."

There was a fit of coughing from the dressing room, and I saw Sechelela and some nurses hugging themselves with glee. With a depressor and a torch, I examined the throat, and then said, in my very best manner:

"Your throat is very red indeed" — as indeed it was — "I think I will *tulu malaka."*

"Ooowhi!" yelled Suzannah, and fled screaming, moving at an amazing pace. The staff rolled on the floor and laughed till they cried.

I couldn't help joining in their amusement, but behind the fun was the grim fact of death and suffering that stalk so closely in the wake of witchcraft and heathen practice.

Other feats of Gogo surgery are catheterization with a crow's feather, and licking the eye to remove foreign bodies.

Tooth removal is done by forcing the blade of a blunt knife under the roots and levering.

Twice we had *Waganga* — witch doctors — in our hospital. Neither would take the native medicine they prescribed for others, and I don't blame them. Lenholo, the first of them, was a miserable specimen, riddled with syphilis. He started to haggle over the fee, but when he heard that a shilling a week covered everything, he was most surprised, and not a little suspicious that he would get only inferior medicine. Free medicine means only one thing to the African. He says: "*Kah!* It can't be much good if you get it for nothing." For this reason we charge nominal fees. He had no more suspicions after his first injection — his temperature shot up to 108, he shivered violently, and in a weak voice, said: "Bwana, *that's* medicine."

In the small hours an agitated dresser called me to see him, and whispered fearfully in my ear: "You know he is a *Muganga,* Bwana!"

In the dimly lighted ward, with the patient's head and all under the blankets, the mutterings of the delirious man were decidedly eerie. I couldn't pick up a word of it, and the dresser was too terrified to tell me what he was saying. As we watched, he stood up in bed, stark naked — a vague silhouette against the whitewashed wall. Pointing his finger at me, he cursed vilely in Gogo. The dresser gasped and fled, while I put the man back into bed and gave him a sedative.

In the next bed to Lenholo was an unfortunate with a liver abscess. Emetine had been given, and I set up everything to aspirate the abscess. With the greatest of interest, Lenholo watched tubes, needles and bottles arrive. I injected some local anesthetic, and pushed a large needle into the liver. The bottle was emptied by a vacuum pump and tubes connected to both needle and bottle. I moved the needle about, and suddenly, with a swish, pus poured into the bottle.

"*Kah!*" exclaimed Lenholo, nearly falling off his bed in his amazement. "That is real magic!"

"*Wacho!* — Rot!" replied the dresser. "That is wisdom."

"*Yah,*" said Lenholo. "We've never seen anything like that anywhere before."

After he went home cured I lost track of his doings, but often wonder if he tried out any of our minor operations, and with what result.

The other *Muganga* was an old woman with a most evil reputation. She was stone blind with cataracts in both eyes. Her son brought her thirty miles on a donkey and bolted, leaving her with us. She was terrified, and screamed for mercy.

"What's up, mother?" I asked her. "What's all the noise about?"

"Who are you?" she asked.

"I'm the doctor."

"A European?"

"Yes."

"But you speak our language."

"Truly, but what are you yelling for? — we won't hurt you."

"She thinks you will be angry because she is a *Muganga,*" said Blandina, the ward sister. "She is the one who ruined people's eyes at Mwitichila."

"*Yaya gwe!* — Don't tell lies!" wailed the old woman. "I'm a poor, blind woman, and I want help to see. Look I've brought my shillings," and from the corner of her black cloth she produced some money.

"How about Masimba, who came here blinded? Why did you not send him to Bwana before you blinded him?"

"*Nasutya!* — I did wrong! Bwana, have mercy," she wailed.

Among the people she was an eye specialist; her treatment was limited to one line. There were three various barks which she collected in the forest. Being confronted by a case, she would chew these up in her mouth — which was foul with stumps of teeth oozing pus — and spit the finished product into her patient's eye. The grossly inflamed eye would swell until it stuck out like an organ stop. A few days later it would take on a dull, angry red, and then burst. The agony suffered must have been terrible.

Months later, forlorn figures, led by a child, would come up to us for treatment, and all I could say was: "It's too late, the eye is ruined."

Blandina told her all this, and more, before she admitted her to hospital. The last I heard was: "Why didn't you try your own medicine on your own eye?" Her operations were a complete success, and she went home, seeing quite well, and with a very different outlook on life.

The most sinister side of a witch doctor's work is the spells he casts. A man pays his cows and goats, and the *Muganga* makes a medicine. All is done in the night.

Then he goes and walks around the victim's house and casts his spells. Perhaps he will leave a few sticks, feathers and a native pot in the path to the house. Perhaps a cock's head, stuffed with medicines, is found near the door.

Whatever it is, the family is terrified, and often calamity comes to them. Everyone is very reticent about talking of this side of a witch doctor's efforts, but they strongly hint that he backs up his charms with poison.

Sheer fright is often enough to kill. My bitterest memory is of a girl upon whom I performed a Caesarian section. The operation went smoothly, and both mother and baby did well, until one morning some old women slipped into the ward and talked to her.

What they said, I shall never know; but this I do know, that within twelve hours of their arrival she was dead. Her pulse which had been normal, faded out, and she died,

I firmly believe, from sheer fright. There was no sign of poison, and nothing to indicate anything unusual medically.

There is a deep strain of the occult in these people; it is very difficult for us to find, or even to appreciate it.

My own personal dealing with native treatment was one day when a branch from a cactus swung back and hit me in the face. The milky juice went into my eye, and the pain was intense. My companion said: "There is only one thing for that, Bwana — human milk." And off he ran. However, I had my emergency kit, and washed out the eye with water from my safari bottle, and had just put in drops to ease pain and relieve congestion, when my African friend came panting up, dragging by the hand a woman who would willingly have helped me in my extremity.

CHAPTER 11

Babies

I FRANKLY had a keen interest in babies, all the more so since Mary, my wife, had a week before presented me with a splendid seven-pound daughter. When the African mothers heard that our new arrival was to be called Rosemary there were a number of small African girls called "Losemelly." Scores of folk came to wish us "*Lusona* — congratulations," and to say all manner of pretty things about the newest white visitor in Tanganyika. The clock informed me that there was still forty minutes before the ten p.m. feeding, so after tucking the mosquito net firmly round the cot, I idly turned the pages of the *British Medical Journal* and read:

"In some parts of India the infantile mortality rate is five to six hundred per thousand." I laid down the paper. Why shouldn't I make a rough survey over here in Central Tanganyika? I had excellent opportunities, and since we had recently cured a painful eye condition for a chief, probably we would find a willing ally in him.

I reached for a pad, and wrote to Nhonya, the chief at Handali, and asked him to send word to two hundred mothers to come in from the thornbush jungle to his mud-brick "palace."

I folded the note, written in my best Chigogo, and looked out over the cornfields to the hills, clearly visible in the brilliant moonlight.

My favorite method of relaxation, after a solid day's work, was classical music. I removed from the phonograph a little nursery rhyme record that had entertained young David during his evening meal, and put on the "Moonlight Sonata." I turned down the hurricane lantern and lay back with a sigh in an armchair which had started its life as a packing case. The music gently carried me into another continent. The third movement was just beginning when, unexpectedly, a voice called harshly: "*Hodi!* — May I come in?"

The spell was broken. I started to my feet, turned up the light, and said, resignedly: "*Karibu* — Come in."

It was old Sechelela, armed with a stick and a hurricane lantern. She smiled at me. "Is Bibi well?" I nodded. "Is Losemelly also well?" I pointed to the cot. She moved quietly to peer in; with a big smile she whispered, "Does Davidi like his new relation?"

"Indeed he does," I said, lighting a hurricane lantern, for a visitation from Sechelela at this hour could mean only one thing — more babies. "What does he say, Bwana?" persisted the old woman. "He says, she is *swamu muno muno* — very, very good," I laughed.

"And your wife's husband thinks so too, *heeh?*"

"*Kumbe,* he does, indeed, Sech, but why do you come to drag me from my family?"

"Our head nurse tapped me on the shoulder. "*Hongo,* more work, Bwana, you must help, for I think it's twins."

I reached for my own knobkerri — snakes rather favor the warmth of the hard-trodden paths through the cornfields — and we walked to the hospital. Above us, standing out gaunt against the starlit sky, were the gnarled, leafless limbs of baobabs; in the distance a jackal's howl followed the braying of donkeys.

I was in front of the old African woman; she walked in silence for a minute, and then said:

"*Agwe! mhola, hola!* — Not so fast!"

I slowed down, and she continued: "My legs are old, remember."

I laughed. "I've just been reading of the days when your legs were young, the days when Bwana Doctor Livingstone walked through the cornfields of Tanganyika. Truly, he had troubles greater than ours."

"*Kah,*" said the old midwife, "there were no hospitals in those days; if there had been, we would not have suffered as we did when my legs were strong."

I swung open the hospital gate for her; she walked through, and suddenly leaped with surprising agility to one side, bringing down her stick with a whack.

"What's up, Sech?"

"*Nje,* Bwana! A scorpion."

We did not stop to view her handiwork, but crossed the moonlit courtyard, mounted some steps, and opened a door. Before us in the maternity ward lay a young African woman, and crouching in a corner, were her old female relatives. They mumbled suspiciously together.

Sechelela took them to task:

"Will you not greet the Bwana?" she challenged.

"*Yah,*" said the dirtier of the two, "but does he know our language and customs?"

"*Mbukwenyi* — Good evening," I said.

"*H-e-e-e,*" they gasped in concert, "truly he knows."

"Now sit there and be quiet," said the old matron.

A trim native nurse helped me with my examination. I ordered treatment, and went into the day room to await developments.

Sechelela and I sat on stools skilfully contrived from gasoline cases by our lame African carpenter.

The old woman yawned.

"*Eehoo!* Bwana. Babies, babies, babies, and babies — sixty-two this month so far, and still five days to go."

"Well, Sech, we've dealt with eight hundred babies this year, and seven years ago the women wouldn't even come near the hospital."

"They come now, Bwana, only because you and the *Wabibi* — the Sisters — speak our language, and understand our customs. Also the people rejoice that you are the father of children. Many have joy to watch your wife with Losemelly and to see the way you look after little

Davidi. Also, Bwana, you train the girls of our tribe to be nurses and leave very much of the work in our hands, only helping when there is real need."

"After all, Sech, it's better that way. You can deal very well with every ordinary case, and I can help when things look a bit difficult."

The old matron had moved over to the window, and suddenly, at the top of her voice, called to the two old hags in the corner:

"You stay there. Don't you dare to move, not one step, not even one."

They shuffled guiltily back to their seats. I grinned.

"That's the way, Sech! Keep 'em in their place."

"*Kah,*" came the reply, "they're a nuisance. Grandmothers are one of the biggest causes of the babies dying like flies here in Tanganyika. If you saw things that I've seen you'd be sick. They say milk is no food for babies, so they cram porridge down the child's throat, even when he is a few days old."

I shuddered. "I have seen them doing it, Sech, and when the baby objected, they just pushed the porridge stuff down all the more enthusiastically."

Sechelela made exasperated noises.

"*Kah!* But think of the number who die — they die like flies. *Kah!*"

"Flies, you say, Sech? Well, I've written tonight to Nhonya at Handali, asking him to help me to find out how many do die out there in the bush, where there is no hospital to help."

"*Viswanu* — a good idea," said Sechelela.

At that moment a call came from the other room. We hurried in, and in half an hour the African nurse unbuttoned my gown and untied my mask, and the population of Ugogo had increased by two. They were fine twins, and their mother was an intelligent girl — an old girl of the C.M.S. Boarding School. I felt those dusky-pink twins had a good chance if only the old women could be kept from their usual tricks.

Before I went home I went over to my patient. I felt her pulse. She smiled up at me:

"Bwana, truly you're being here is the goodness of God. I would have suffered for days unless you had helped."

"*Mbeka* — Surely," said the nurse, "the Bwana knows what to do, and does it."

A fortnight later, Sechelela and I set out for Handali. As we arrived in the little wind-swept town it was obvious that the chief had done his part. The forecourt of his mud-brick, mud-roofed house was packed with women and babies and dogs. Some of those women had never seen a European before.

They looked at me in amazement, and laughed.

"Look," said one, "his hair doesn't curl. It's straight. Look at his eyes. They're green!"

With an effort, I kept my face straight.

Another woman said: "I know about these Europeans. They've got white faces, white hands and white legs, but they're black under their shirts."

"*Anye,*" I said, in the native language, "remember that even Europeans have ears."

"*Yah,*" they whispered, "he speaks Chigogo."

"We're black under our shirts, are we? Well, what do you think of that?" and proceeded to pull up my shirt.

"*Yah! Yah! Yah!*" they cried. "Behold he *is* white, even under his shirt!"

Amazement on every hand gave place to high-pitched laughter.

"*Koh!*" said one woman, with a baby peering over her shoulder. "Behold, he knows how to laugh."

I had done much by that simple act to gain their confidence.

They sat in little groups under thorn trees, or in the shade of a giant baobab tree, talking and laughing. Toddlers, with bells around their ankles, played with the dogs and rolled in the dust. Women, with babies on their backs, sat around gossiping, or squatted with their legs wide apart. Others cooked porridge or gruel in clay pots over an open fire. I saw Africa as it had been for centuries.

A room in the chief's "palace" was specially prepared for us. The furniture was three gasoline cases. It sounds imposing when I say that it was a room in the chief's palace, but actually it was a gloomy enclosure, with mud roof, mud walls, and a cow-dung-plastered floor. A hen and her chickens scuttled to the other end as we entered. The floor had been washed for our coming, and pools of highly pungent water were constant reminders of the chief's herd. A large cowskin in the corner was the examination table, and flies were thick. Fortunately, the walls were in a state of disrepair, and this gave us some light. I sat on one gasoline case, and used the other as a table, and Sechelela, the old African matron, sat opposite.

"You had better let me ask the questions, Bwana, because, even though your Chigogo is not too bad, many of them will not listen to you, because they think that a European can speak only English."

"All right," I said, "you go straight ahead."

"Also," she said, "if you ask them questions, they will tell you lies, because no one likes to admit their faults, but they won't lie to me, because I know all their tricks."

Behind us was a native nurse, armed with a huge bottle of cough mixture of a rich brown color, and another, a mild aperient, tinted blue, and a third of "stomach medicine," colored bright pink. The women would not have come without this inducement, and they were overjoyed to taste our medicine.

The questions were very simple, and each woman was asked the same things.

"How many children have you had?"

"How many died?"

"Why did they die?"

I will never forget one woman. She was prematurely old, and had a haggard look. On her back was a three year old child, whose head seemed too heavy for its neck.

"Why are you carrying him?" asked Sechelela.

"Behold, he cannot yet walk."

I examined his legs. They were flail-like, and swung limply from his knees. His ribs protruded, and his outer bones stuck out painfully. He was a mass of skin disease. A case of advanced rickets and malnutrition!

"How many other children have you had?"

"Oh, sixteen," she said.

"And where are they?"

"Dead," she replied, shaking her head, "all dead."

"How old were your children when they died?" asked Sechelela.

"Most of them died before their teeth came. They died *bwete* — for no cause at all."

"What did the old women say?"

"Oh, they said my milk was bad, so I fed them on porridge, but it did no good. They all died."

Sechelela turned to her and said: "Go in there and you will get your medicine."

She looked across to me and said: "Do you wonder they all die, Bwana?"

Another woman said she had twelve children. Two were alive. All the others had died. Some died from measles. Three from *mhungo* — malaria. And then, as an afterthought, "O course, two were no person; I have not counted them."

"No person, Sech?" I said. "What's that?"

"Well, Bwana, if a baby is very small when it's born, and the old women say it will not live, then they put it outside to die. It's not worth working for. It's 'no person' — even if it is crying lustily. Sometimes, perhaps, if a baby is born and is not breathing, again it's 'no person' and left to die."

"Well, and we save nearly every one in our hospital."

"Yes," agreed the old African matron, "but 'in our hospital' is very different. Our way is a better way. We follow the laws of God and of wisdom."

And so it went on the whole morning. Woman after woman, with her story of death and sorrow and suffering. We tried to trace the cause. Many had obviously died from malaria, and nearly every baby I saw that day had a big spleen sticking out obviously below its skinny ribs. Others had died in the vast measles and meningitis epidemics that had swept the country, carrying off hundreds of babies. But by far the greatest number had died because of neglect and the hopeless outlook of the African woman on the diet necessary for infants.

I had covered five pages with statistics when Sechelela said:

"Let's stop for a while, Bwana, and have a cup of tea. My tongue is as dry as the desert."

I filled two cups from the thermos, and offered her sugar. She took five teaspoonfuls, stirred vigorously, and drank enthusiastically, if unmusically. From where we were sitting, I could see the women outside through a crack in the mud wall. One woman had a clay pot full of thick gruel of a grey tint, looking like dirty, cold starch. On her knee was a small baby, less than a month old. She scooped up a handful of this revolting-looking native porridge, propped the child's mouth open, and pushed the food into the small mouth, and rammed it down her infant's throat with an enthusiastic thumb. The child spluttered and coughed, but the mother placidly continued, only stopping when the child's tummy was protruding sufficiently to assure her that the baby had had enough "food."

I looked across at Sechelela.

"Do you wonder they die, Bwana?"

"Did they do that to you, Sech?"

She threw her head back and laughed! "I don't remember, Bwana, but I know, in the days when I was heathen, before the pioneers told me about Jesus and His love, that I lost my first two children by feeding them that way. How can we know a better way, unless we're told?"

I filled up her cup again. "Tell me, Sech, do you feel our work helps your people? Do you feel they want to know about Jesus, and of the way out of sin that He bought for them with His blood?"

The old matron put her hand on my shoulder. "Bwana, for forty years I have been a Christian. My husband beat me, and twice my relatives tried to poison me because I chose to follow my Savior. Would I have done that if I had not believed that only Jesus can solve the troubles and sadnesses of my people? If you feel down-hearted, Bwana, look at the difference between these women here and their children, and the Christian women and their children. Truly, following Jesus is the only practical, worthwhile way of living."

She set down her cup. We opened the door again. I stood there looking at the women. Many of them had walked twenty miles over narrow tracks through the thorn-bush. It was a quaint sight to see them, dressed for the most part in a yard or two of black cloth, wound skirt fashion around their waists. Many had babies on their backs, held there by an ingenious contraption made from cowhide. Their heads were shaved. I was wondering why, when Sechelela came to my side.

"Why do they shave off their hair, Sech?"

"*H-e-e!*" said she, raising her eyebrows, "if they do that, to what can the lice hold?"

I asked no more questions after that.

For a moment longer I took in the scene. There were more than a hundred women still to be seen. All had their ears pierced, with round wooden ornaments inserted. On their ankles were pounds of brass ornaments. But the most outstanding thing about them was the gracefulness of their poise. Their daily tasks of carrying firewood and great calabashes of water on their heads have given them a grace of movement that would be the envy of many a women at home.

For four more hours I listened to a story of the stark tragedy of African motherhood and child life. That evening I sat at my desk and worked out statistics. I had reached my final figures. I couldn't believe them, so I checked them over once again, with the same result. I whistled softly.

"What's the matter?" said my wife.

"Phew! I'd never have believed it unless I had seen it with my own eyes. Do you know that seven hundred and eighty out of every thousand of the babies born out there in the bush die before they reach even their first birthday? It's the hopeless ignorance of the old women of the tribe. We've got to get down to it and train African girls as nurses and welfare workers. We simply can't let this go on and complacently watch eight out of every ten babies die."

A month later I went to an Old Girls' rally at the Mvumi Girls' Boarding School and met a hundred ex-pupils, all neatly dressed in African fashion. Many had their children with them.

Once again Sechelela and I sat down and asked our string of questions. But this time there was a different story.

These girls had had training in child welfare. They had been taught to feed a baby and to bathe it, and to avoid the worst of native practices. For the most part their children were healthy and prosperous. Few had malaria, and I was struck by the absence of skin disease, which always seems to go hand-in-hand with malnutrition. Many of the girls had come to our hospital to have their infants.

One girl, a teacher, had her twins with her — one on her back and one clinging around her neck. Strangely enough, these children were the first I had helped into the world in Tanganyika, and I had dubbed them "Ping" and "Pong." It is a very unusual thing for twins to survive in this part of Africa. The mother sees that one is stronger than the other and takes more care of it, and the second one just fades away and soon dies from sheer neglect.

Amongst the children there I saw four premature infants who, in the everyday way of things, would have been left to die, but who now were larger and better-looking in every way than many normal children born at the same time.

Out of curiosity, I took ten children of the hospital helpers and sent out to the village to get ten children of the same age. I sat them down in the sun and looked at them critically. There was no comparison between the two groups. The children who had been looked after according to the principles of mothercraft were stronger, healthier and more cheerful-looking than those who had been brought up by native methods. Of the hospital children, not one had died, while the village children represented the "survival of the fittest" in their native homes. Several of them had pronounced rickets. They showed the classical signs; the head of the philosopher, the chest of the greyhound, the "tummy" of a poisoned pup, and the legs of a grand piano. I called the girls together and showed them the difference, and said:

"What is the reason?"

They answered in chorus: "Breast feed is the best feed, and nothing but milk till the teeth appear."

Once again, that evening I sat at my desk and went through my figures. What a comparison! In the untaught native mothers' homes, well over seven hundred babies out of every thousand had died; in the Old Girls of the School, the figure was under one hundred and ninety. By simple instruction, quite apart from medical treatment, we had made amazing progress towards building a healthier and a better type of African baby in the plains of Central Tanganyika.

CHAPTER 12

Welfare Focused

THERE was a light in the kitchen doorway. I walked wearily back from the hospital.

"*O . . y!* Tim," I called. "*Unozereze chai lulu baha* —Make tea straight away!"

"*Heya,* Bwana!" came the cheerful voice.

I sent my helmet spinning on to a table that had once been a packing case, and sank down with relief into a comfortable chair. My wife looked up from the *Tanganyika Standard* — the local weekly that kept us in touch with the outside world. She turned up the kerosene lamp, and said:

"You've had a strenuous time?"

"Ugh," I said, "eight hours of it. But she's all right now. It was Yuditi, you know, and her first infant. It's a funny thing how these educated girls seem to have so much more trouble than the bush people. I'm glad all the other eight hundred that arrive each year aren't like her. *E-e-e-h-o-o-o,* I'm tired."

"What was her baby like?"

"Oh, a miserable specimen, prematurish, and under four pounds. The old ladies who practise in the villages would have thrown it out as not worth the trouble of looking after. We've got it wrapped up in cotton-wool and lying on a hot brick. I think it will pull round all right. It's a boy, and is to be called John."

Mary, woman-like, went to look for a pair of bootees and other mysterious garments, while I drank tea from an enormous cup. Timothy would never go home till I came back from the hospital, and always he produced some tid-bit to tempt even the most jaded appetite.

"Much work these days, Bwana?"

"Truly," I replied. "Sometimes, Tim, I wish I were twins. Then I could do twice as much work."

He laughed, and he produced his famous dish — chicken cutlets.

A few minutes later I was looking at a collection of baby woollens, and picking out those I thought would fit.

"By the way, do you remember that woman that used to bring our firewood — the hopeless soul who could never follow our instructions? Ndudula was her name."

My wife nodded. "Well, she came to all Yuditi's classes and did absolutely nothing that she was told, and now she has produced a large infant without any trouble at all. There they lie in the hospital on the same side of the ward — Yuditi, the welfare teacher, with her puny infant, and in the next bed is Ndudula, who did everything that she should not have done, and she has a splendid ten-pounder. It's hard to understand."

"Hodi?" said a voice.

"Karibu!" Once again it was old Sechelela. I brought her a three-legged stool and she sat down; obviously she had some important information and was bursting to tell it.

"Well, Sech," said my wife, "what's the news?"

But Sechelela was far too polite to tell the news before she had inquired after our health and that of our children.

"Come on," I said. "Tell me the news. You look like a bee in a bottle."

"H-e-e-e-e," said Sechelela. "A bee in a bottle, indeed. I have news, Bwana, that will rejoice your heart, and make you laugh deep down in your stomach. You know, all the old women of the tribe have been casting spells on Yuditi. They are full of rejoicing, and say that now she will know that it's better to follow Gogo customs than the strange ways of Europeans. They say, Bibi, that her child will die, because do not all children die that look like hers when they are born? And now everybody in the village waits to see

little John die, and then the old women will have scored a great victory."

I nodded.

"Then they say: "Look at Ndudula. Was she not *musugu?* — a cunning one. Did she not go to the classes so that she would get a shirt for her baby? But did she not secretly follow the advice of the *wadala* — the old women?"

"Yuditi's baby will be all right, Sech."

"I think so, too, Bwana, but hadn't we better make sure?"

I nodded, and we knelt down and asked God to protect that baby from any misadventure and to help us to use this incident greatly for gaining the confidence of the people and spreading the Good News.

On my round next day, I found that all was well. The child, I felt certain, would thrive. I told Yuditi so. She beamed, and said:

"Bwana, will you advance me seven-and-sixpence?"

"All right," I said, "what for?"

"An alarm clock. How can I know when it is six, ten, two, six and ten, if I have not a clock? The people in the jungle tell the time by the sun. But behold, there's no sun at ten o'clock at night."

"Truly, Yuditi, but how can the other women know the time?"

She smiled. "Have we not a drum in the town, and can that drum not be heard for eight miles? When it's time to feed the baby, my small brother-in-law will beat the drum."

It was just about the time when Mr. Churchill had brought in the "V for Victory" campaign, so I suggested that the drummer should drum out ". . . — . . . —" when it was time to feed the baby!

Week after week went by, and baby John thrived and thrived. His mother, within a week, was back on the job, giving welfare lectures and weighing babies, filling in baby weight cards, and doing all her routine duties, with her small infant on her back, or lying asleep in the cot which his father had made, following our fathercraft class. It was a stout affair, made from bush timber and local vines, with hoops put over the top for a mosquito net to keep away the flies. The women gazed at this new idea.

"Oh," they said, "why not carry him on your back all day?"

"He sleeps better there," said Yuditi.

"*Kah,*" said the women, "that is not our custom."

"No," said Yuditi, "nor is it your baby; this is a better way."

"Oh," they said, "tell us about it."

So she explained the principles of mothercraft.

One morning I was doing eye operations. I had just pulled off my mask and cap when I heard a "*Hodi*" at the door, and in walked Yuditi.

"*Mbukwa,* Bwana."

"*Mbukwa,* Yuditi."

"Bwana, it is three months today since John was born. Come and compare him with little Ndudula."

The two babies lay side by side in the welfare room. John was nearly eight pounds, while his rival was eleven. But he showed signs of early rickets. Twice a day he was crammed full with millet gruel. His mother fed him in the natural way only to keep him quiet.

"What do the old women of the village say now, Yuditi?"

"They say many things, Bwana, but not as loudly as before."

I sat down to listen to the instructions being given regarding tomato juice, and I smiled as I thought of my water carrier, who grew tomatoes near his house. With the greatest pride he had shown me his crop — three straggly bushes, surrounded by thorn bush to keep away inquisitive and hungry chickens.

"*Yah,*" he remarked, "are they not fine plants? And I have had many tomatoes. Some are as big as a child's fist.

Others were as big as marbles, and then there were lots and lots of little ones!"

But these native-grown tomatoes, when crushed, supply the vitamins so necessary for the health of the children of the country.

Some weeks later, at harvest time, I went out into the garden in the early morning to have a look around. There, in his cot, was John. His father and mother were working vigorously in the garden. In the next garden was Ndudula. On her back was her baby. I looked at the two children. John was heavier and infinitely healthier. Yuditi saw me making the comparison, and smiled.

"The old women are strangely silent these days, Bwana. But the young women are not. They say: 'Behold, is there any profit in seeing all your children die? Is it not better to follow this way of wisdom?' They all thought my baby would die, but they see now that, with care, and by doing what any one of them can do, my baby has lived, and is better, much better, than Ndudula's."

Later that morning, in the clinic, Yuditi was talking to the mothers from the village. They had all arrived with their children, bringing their baby weight cards. Many of them could not write, nor understand the figures on them, but they could understand the graph in red pencil that showed the child was growing stronger and stronger, and heavier and heavier week by week. They looked with the greatest interest at the welfare pictures which Yuditi displayed. There was one of ten African babies. Each baby fitted into slots in the cardboard.

"Listen!" said the teacher. "This child" — she pulled the first one from its slot — "was fed on gruel from the day he was born, and he only saw the light of the sun for three weeks, and then he died, because he was given the wrong food."

"*Yah,*" said the audience, "nine left."

"Stop, that's what I do!" cried one woman. Her neighbors prodded her in the ribs. "Be quiet! Do you want to advertise that all your children have died?"

"This child was given water from the well, and behold, there were germs in the water. They poisoned the child, and he died."

"*Kah!*" said a woman from the back. "I give my child water from the well. Will it do him harm?"

"It will," said Yuditi. "Take a small clay pot and boil the water. Cover the pot with a piece of cloth to keep out the flies, and your child will be safe."

She pulled out the third baby.

"This child was not fed on milk. His legs grew weak, his head was too heavy for his neck. He had no strength in his body. A mosquito bit him, and he died from *mbungo* — malaria. Remember — 'Breast feed is best feed, and no porridge till the teeth come.'"

And so it went on and on. The women were taught in a way they could understand, by one of their own tribe, who had given them the best example of all, in that her own baby had been brought up following what she taught, and he was the most outstanding child in the whole village.

CHAPTER 13

Kilimatinde

THERE were dozens of small boys tremendously interested by something that was going on in my garage. I strolled up to see, and found all the tools were laid out on a pack, and my driver was oiling and greasing the jack. He got to his feet.

"We shall want some new patches at once, sir. We have only got enough for ten punctures."

"How many shall we get on the way to Kilimatinde, Samson?"

"Perhaps only three or four, but remember the Kongwa safari, when we had eighty-two."

It was after that trip that I missed the root extraction forceps from the dental kit in the operating room, and, after a thorough search, at last found them in the tool chest. I asked Samson:

"What are these doing in the car?"

"Do I not use them for taking out the thorns from the inside of the tires, sir?" he replied.

As we were packing up tools and equipment, a junior dresser arrived with a sterilizer full of instruments, and a nurse followed him with a pack of sterile surgery linen on her head. Everything was carefully packed in dust-proof boxes. Timothy, the cook, then turned up with a canvas water bag and two full water bottles. We put in the hoes and the spades, the axes and the towing rope. All was ready.

"Well, Samson, we will leave at the crack of dawn tomorrow."

The driver grinned. "Yes, sir," he replied; and as I walked up to the hospital to do an evening round of the wards, I heard him tell the cook to wake Bwana early, as it was a long safari and he wanted to get there by noon.

The next morning I was awakened by the cook's assistant bringing me a cup of tea. It was pitch dark.

"Safari today, Bwana. Here is your tea."

Grumbling mightily, I peered at my watch by the light of his hurricane lantern. It was two a.m.!

"Clear out, will you!" I mumbled sleepily. "It is still night."

He departed, chuckling.

It was barely light when finally we set out.

Early mornings are wonderful in Ugogo. The sunrises are a marvelous harmony of golds and reds, and the air is cold and stimulating. We drove through a brown thornbush forest; knob-billed birds screeched and flapped their wings as we approached, and a jackel looked curiously at us from behind an ant hill.

In the back of the truck was an old one-eyed man with a tattered cloth tied round his shoulders, and two of the village belles, dressed in the gaudy cloths sold by Indian storekeepers. Grandfather clocks, Union Jacks, anchors and amorous inscriptions in Arabic, Swahili, and English, all fought for a place on a square yard of material. Apart from one tiny tuft, their heads were close shaven and rubbed with oil.

Along the Cape to Cairo road clouds of fine red dust, choking and smothering, swirled into the car. Through a haze stood out a little hill crowned with a huge granite boulder, and below it lay Dodoma, the main Government post of the Central Province.

My passengers scrambled over the back of the car. The old man's wrinkles were a delicate tracery of powdery dust; the girls' great brown eyes peered ludicrously through a thick layer of red.

"*Assante*, Bwana — Thank you, sir."

"Well, good bye," I said. "Shop successfully, and we shall see one another again."

Driving cautiously through a narrow street, thronged with people of every creed and tribe, past the market where astute Indian merchants bought hides and beeswax from half naked, mud-in-haired natives, we stopped at a ramshackle *godown*.

I sat waiting while the stout Indian storekeeper routed out two cases of gasoline. His shop opened directly on to the street, and the view from it was like a movie travelog. Women passed with huge bundles of firewood, weighing over a hundred pounds, on their heads. Four lithe, turbaned Somalilanders, wearing striped blazers, glaring scarves, and multi-colored sarongs, played cards under a tree. Over the way were a Hindu bootmaker sitting tailor-fashion, and a Sikh carpenter, sawing back to front.

It was a kaleidoscope of Africa and Asia, with the inevitable crow and goat — the latter with an absurd blue print bag tied over its udder — as background.

With horn blaring in approved Indian style, I nosed my way through narrow streets, cluttered with every variety of native shop selling all manner of goods. Indian, African and Arab children scampered to safety at our approach. Swinging into a wider road, we passed the beer market — the most festering spot in Dodoma, the breeding ground of crime and a rendezvous for thieves and prostitutes.

It was a relief to see again the dusty road twisting its way over the plain, which by now was shimmering and glaring in the sun. Samson — my clerk, driver and general utility man — was at the wheel. We had backed into a tangled mass of thorn to let two bullock carts, with crazy, wobbly wheels, pass. The poor old bus skidded alarmingly in the deep sand; Samson pulled up, and resignedly got out the jack. Not twenty yards away was a towering wedge of granite fifty feet high, the only shade for miles. I collected some sticks, and soon had some water boiling and the tea ready by the time Samson came to show me a huge thorn that he had dragged from the tire with the dental forceps.

I took the wheel, and nearly brought disaster upon the safari. We had passed a dry lake and a mixed herd of fat-tailed sheep and humpbacked cattle optimistically hunting for pickings on the brown, dry hillside, and were watching an eagle soaring overhead, when, suddenly turning sharply round a giant ant hill, we came on a wild pig's hole, two feet deep, and directly in the path of the car. I swerved violently, grazed a stump on the near side, and just got through. My companion snorted in disgust and shook his head.

"These wild porks, sir!"

Out came the hoe from the mud-fighting outfit, and we filled in the hole with stones and earth.

Suddenly the country began to change: dust gave place to deep sand, and palm trees appeared. In the distance, over the white shimmering plain, was the blue Rift Wall, and just before us the palm-thatched houses of Bahi.

Samson is a Musukuma, of a tribe that comes from near the Lakes. He wanted to buy some fish. I laughed.

"Fish here! Why, there isn't any water for miles."

"But, sir, they dig them up with a spade!"

I laughed again.

"I wouldn't draw your foot, sir."

"You wouldn't what, Samson?"

The African looked blankly at me. He opened his mouth to reply, but before he spoke I realized what he meant to say.

I chuckled: "The right idiom is 'to pull the leg.' "

Samson rolled his eyes humorously. He pulled up outside a palm-thatched native shop, inside which were strings of dried mudfish, incredibly bony. This strange creature digs in when the black soil plains dry up, and lives deep down till the next rains turn the flats into a vast, shallow lake.

The Bahi River, which, in the rains, is a roaring menacing torrent, was nothing but a long, shallow drift in the forest,

At Mvumi Hospital

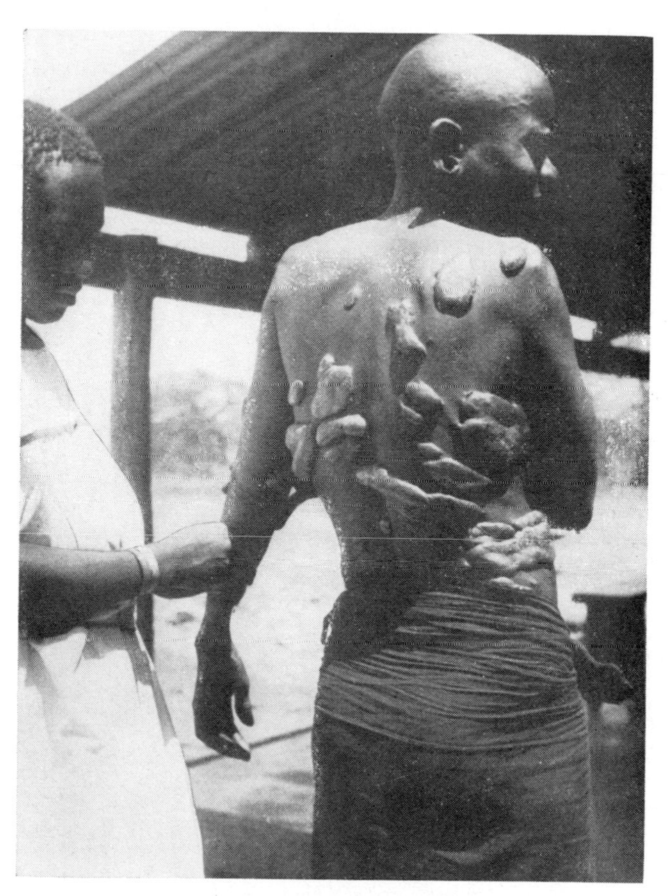

WITCH DOCTOR'S SCARS

The huge keloid scars, "like mountains on a huge relief map," are the work of the witch doctor. "Once *they are there, nothing can be done. Remove them, and they re-turn bigger and less treatable." (Witchcraft and Native Medicine)*

Outpatient's Department,
Mvumi Base Hospital

Pulling Down the
Old Men's Ward,
Mvumi Hospital

Re-building with
Sun-dried Mud Bricks

overhung by tall trees, whose monkey population swung deeper into the bush as the car rattled over a road of hardened hoofprints. Beside us was a causeway dating back to the days of German chain gang labor.

Turning between some patriarchal baobabs, we surprised six fine gazelle. They were beautiful creatures, and I could not resist swinging off the road and chasing them over the plain, dodging between trees and ant hills. They bounded high into the air, clearing great bushes and boulders in their stride. In the excitement of the chase, I forgot the road, and, with wheels locked, just managed to pull up on the very edge of a deep hole. We slowly made our way back through a mass of thorn trees, and came out of the bush on to the road again. The glare was almost blinding, and the wind scorched us.

In this barren, shadeless spot we had our second puncture. Samson jacked up the wheel, and I took off the spare and the punctured wheel. I screwed the punctured wheel on to the side while Samson tightened the bolts and removed the jack. Six minutes' work and we were away again, and very thankful that we had mended the previous puncture.

An Arab village in the midst of a plantation of mango trees was a most welcome patch of green. While restful to the eye, these great, shady trees bring back memories of the old days. You are very safe in saying that wherever you find mango trees planted, there the Arab slave-traders have been. The Lake ports of Ujiji and Mwanza, and the famous inland town of Tabora, where Livingstone and Stanley lived together for a time, are all on the slave route, and are plentifully planted with mango trees.

Ahead of us was a stiff climb up an unfenced pass to the top of the great Rift Wall. Within half a mile the plain changes to dense forest.

On these hills, with a hundred-mile view of the plain, is our large Leper Colony. My colleague, Dr. Cyril Wallace, who is both padre and physician, has some two hundred and fifty lepers, in all stages of the disease, under his care. The untainted children are separated from the parents, and live on the top of the hill, where they have lessons in ordinary school work, as well as in agriculture and arts and crafts. They are near their relatives, and can often see them, but are not in direct contact, which, under unhygienic circumstances, spells almost certain infection. Danger lies, not in the pathetic folk, with gnarled features and fingerless stumps of hands; in these the disease is largely burnt out. It is the apparently healthy cases, with only a patch or two of the disease, who are literally swarming with the leprosy bacillus, who spread the scourge.

In this model colony, each family has its own specially built hut. As far as he is able, each man is encouraged to cultivate his garden or to do some handicraft. Specific injections, rubbings with chaulmoogra oil, and good diet, made a marked change in their condition, and very many are now symptom free. I saw one family, the father of which was a pathetic sight — fingerless and toeless, his face bulbous and distorted with disease. One son was infected, but was still in an early stage. On his back a great yellow patch showed where the leprosy bacillus was playing havoc. Up the hill I saw two younger children, both free from the disease, and fine little folk. They had just come from school to greet their father and brother. I could not but notice the gap of two yards which the father insisted be kept between himself and his daughters. All those healthy children on the hill would almost certainly have been infected with leprosy but for this mutually acceptable arrangement whereby families are separated, as far as the disease goes, but have, at the same time, the opportunity of being near each other.

Over a cup of tea, Dr. Wallace told me how, a few days previously, he had gone out to shoot some pig that had been raiding the people's sweet-potato gardens. Seeing a movement in the bush, he got his sights on the animal, which suddenly moved into view. He fired, and a great, tawny lion sprang into the air and fell dead, not twenty feet from him. A big game hunter once told me that you have nothing to fear from a lion if he is not hungry. While believing this, I have not yet found out how to estimate a lion's hunger.

I seem to be the only doctor on this job who has not shot a lion. My predecessor, Dr. Murray Buntine, shot one from his dining-room window, and another that blocked his path on the main road. My only experience with a lion seems rather tame to look back on, although I got more than a thrill out of it at the time. I was out shooting guinea-fowl in the late afternoon, and was walking through a tall grass with a hospital dresser.

"That's a funny smell, Mika," I said.

He stopped, sniffed, gasped one word: "*Simba* — Lion!" and fled through the undergrowth. I followed hard on his track. To our left we heard the roar of an animal and saw a tail erect above the grass. We were traveling very fast, when suddenly a hole opened up directly in front of us, and we both fell headlong. Starting to my feet, I saw a huge hog standing in a small clearing. Mika saw it too. He carefully pulled a thorn out of his arm, and, looking up, caught my eye. With a grin, he remarked:

"We weren't afraid, were we, Bwana?"

But even if I had not actually met any of the menagerie that inhabit that particular district, I had quite a time helping those who had. In three weeks' residence at Kilimatinde Hospital I treated a small boy who had been scalped by a hyena; saw a child whose abdomen had been ripped open by a baboon; treated two snake bites, and operated on a man who had been shot in the spleen by a barbed arrow when hunting.

There were well over a hundred outpatients to be seen each day. Unassisted, I removed a number of cataracts; but the highlights of my stay were the ears. Amongst the Wagogo it is a tribal custom to pierce the ears, knock out the two lower front teeth, and burn a scar in the center of the forehead. Many of the local teachers were self-conscious about their ear lobes, which often were large enough to hold a tennis ball. They could not understand how I could cut their flesh without causing pain, and, although they badly wanted to undergo the operation, none of them dared to be the first to have this done. At last, however, one lad — the smallest — was pushed forward. He lay on the table and anxiously awaited proceedings. I injected each end of his long ear lobes with a local anesthetic, and then took a needle and stuck it right through the area for operation. The patient had his eyes fast shut.

"What did you feel?" anxiously inquired the next on the waiting list.

"Nothing," replied the patient. "Why?"

Then he opened his eyes and saw the needle. "*Kah!*" he said. "Truly Bwana did not lie. There is no pain."

At this, there were murmurs of approval from the others. Then my patient, armed with two mirrors, indicated what he wanted in size and shape. At the end, all were tremendously pleased with the results, and went home bursting to show off their new appearance.

Twenty babies arrived while I was there. One mother, a hunchback, gave me a worrying time. I prepared the delivery room, and was ready for any trouble, but a perfectly normal baby arrived quite safely. These native women seem to be made of elastic and over and over again the textbook is made to look silly. Apparently hopeless cases give not the slightest trouble.

The most dramatic case was that of an old woman who had fallen off the roof of her house and broken a thigh. She was carried fifty miles on an upturned native bed, to be brought to the hospital. Imagine the agony as her husband and sons carried her for three days in this manner, stumbling through rivers and dense forest! Without X-raying, we set the fracture, and, in just over a month, she walked home. It was little short of a miracle.

Kilimatinde is a town with a history. It is on the old slave route from the Lakes to Bagamoyo, on the coast. It still has its Arab population, and at sundown little groups of bearded and turbaned men sit on the verandas of their sun-dried, black mud-roofed houses and read the Koran in a sing-song chant, and go through the elaborate ritual of their devotions.

The ruins of a big German fort are between the town and the hospital. A wonderful avenue of trees leads up to its front gate, where the German colors are still visible on a decaying sentry box. One evening my houseboy, Zebedee, and an ancient appropriately named Noah, walked with me to look at the ruins. Noah stopped before a tall tree.

"Here, Bwana, I have often seen men hanging by the neck."

"What were they hanged for?"

"Oh, for stealing cattle or for any of those things for which the British Bwana Shauri, the Administrative Officer, gives three months in jail now."

He shrugged his shoulders and spat. We climbed the wall, and, through a tangle of weeds and rotting machinery, he showed me a courtyard.

"In the middle there was a post, Bwana, where they gave *hamsishirini.*"

"What's that?"

"Twenty-five lashes over the bare back with a *kiboko* — a hippo-hide whip! That was the price for not saluting a German soldier or for refusing to carry a load."

My houseboy, who stood beside me, suddenly spat viciously, and said: "Well I know it! Look!"

He pulled up his shirt, and on his back were great criss-cross scars.

"What happened, Zeb?" I asked.

"I was only a boy at the time of the last war, but the Germans caught me, and told me to carry a box. It was very heavy. I walked all the morning, but in the afternoon I could not go on. They ordered me to carry it, but I could not. Then they flogged me till I fainted." Again he turned and spat.

At one stage a part of this fort had been used as a temporary hospital, but now all that remains of a proud German fort is a crumbling ruin, overgrown with grass, and a haunt for snakes and hyenas.

Two German cemeteries are still kept up by the authorities. I noted that not one of the Ludwigs, Heinrichs or Wilhelms had lived longer than three years after his arrival in Africa. There are ruins of elaborate beer-gardens overlooking the plain, and huge pits, from which the Wagogo still dig bottles. Perhaps the swarms of local malarial mosquitoes found Bacchus a stout ally and gave German tombstone masons a busy time.

Many things combine here to relieve the monotony: an invasion of your house by ants in military formation; the huge footprints of an elephant near the river behind the hospital; the brilliant colors of the sunbirds, and the bright yellow weaver-birds that chatter noisily around their snake-proof nets. At night myriad glowworms twinkle, and hyenas utter their ghastly laugh. The house seems to shake at times with the deep-throated roar of a lion at close quarters.

Late one afternoon a telegram arrived by runner:

> Return immediately. Sister gone to coast with acute appendicitis.

I packed hastily, set the job in order, and left a long list of instructions. It was late in the evening before I had finished everything, and the moon had not risen when we left Kilimatinde. It was intensely dark. In the thickest part of the forest the headlights picked out great piles of elephant dung, still steaming. On the windshield I seemed to see focused a photograph of an elephant shot by an African game scout in the hospital garden not fifty yards from the surgery room. Then I imagined I could hear a crashing in the trees. A great baboon dashed in front of us and vanished in the darkness. Greenish lights in the trees were the eyes of numerous small monkeys. The moon rose over the distant hills. The plain was bathed in soft light and palm trees were silhouetted darkly against the skyline.

In a place where the trees met overhead and we seemed to be moving in a long tunnel of light, a leopard suddenly sprang up from the undergrowth, ran for some distance before us, and then disappeared as suddenly as he had appeared.

At midnight we drove through a silent Dodoma, past market, mosque and cathedral, and there, not a hundred yards from the center of the town, I saw a splendid koodoo bull, nonchalantly strolling past the police lines.

I negotiated thirty miles of the Cape to Cairo road and its equally famous corrugations, then fourteen dry river beds, and at last the white buildings of Mvumi stood out clearly against the dark sky.

Ten minutes later I tumbled into bed. My last memory before sleep came was of the local donkeys braying at the moon.

I had been in bed less than an hour when, just before dawn, I was called to the hospital to save the life of an asphyxiated baby.

I was inexpressibly tired, and fell asleep during my breakfast, and again during morning prayers at the hospital. The staff got up very quietly and tip-toed out, thinking I had some special matter to pray over. A quarter of an hour later, Daudi, hearing a cross between a snort and a snore — which he regarded as not being a devotional sound — decided it was time to wake me.

CHAPTER 14

When the Doctor Is Nurse

THE STRAIN of hospital life is tremendous for the European nurses. On them falls the supervision of the staff, training girls whose background is completely African, battling with relatives, and frequently having to deal with problems that would worry a doctor. Add to this the rigors of the climate, frequent night calls, continuous warfare against the thousands of insects and the tropical diseases they carry, and you will understand how it is that nurse after nurse cracks up on the job.

We were supposed to have two young nursing Sisters at Mvumi and for three months after my arrival we had. The work was progressing at a great pace when the grimness of African conditions first came home to me.

It was four o'clock one morning: I received a note —

Hemorrhage — PPH — Quick.

I dressed hurriedly, buttoning and belting as I ran to the hospital in the starlight. It was a difficult case, but after an hour's intense work I felt the pulse. Our patient was out of danger, and the junior nurse started to bathe the baby.

One small incident in that drama escaped notice, the bite of a stray mosquito. As the Sister worked, gloved and gowned, fighting for that woman's life, her attention was riveted to the job. A week later came headache, shiverings, a feeling of utter tiredness, and then an acute rise in temperature. After hours of the greatest discomfort she felt like a furnace, and then, lying wrapped in blankets, she streamed perspiration. She had contracted malignant malaria, and, although we had the answer to it, she had a very stormy convalescence, and had to be invalided away for three months' sick leave.

The other Sister and I carried on. It was a particularly busy time. The maternity work was booming, and often we had half a dozen operations a day. At the same time, there were lectures to be given to the staff and weekly welfare visits to be made to the villages.

One morning, in a dirty hut, the Sister came upon a young girl covered with foul ulcers. She got to work and bathed and bandaged them, but, as she knelt beside the cowskin upon which the girl lay, she was bitten by a tick. This insect, which is as big as your thumbnail, carries relapsing fever, a disease of danger to an African, and frequently fatal with Europeans.

For ten days she carried on, but all the time the parasites of the disease were breeding in her blood. One morning her houseboy reported that she was saying queer things. I found her delirious, with a temperature of 105°. I took a blood slide and examined it, and found nothing, so we treated her for malaria, and she became worse. Anxiously, Daudi and I examined blood films each day. On the fifth occasion I saw among the confetti-like blood cells a tangle of corkscrew-shaped parasites. Injections of prepared arsenic were given, and the temperature fell. But so intense had been the disease that the unfortunate nurse had to return to Australia. It was nearly two years before she was fit again to take up duty in the plains of Central Tanganyika.

The relieving nurse arrived, and we settled down to a restricted program. When all seemed to be going smoothly once more, she developed acute appendicitis, with complications, and had to be invalided home.

I found myself running the hospital alone, with no prospect of getting a Sister to supervise the nursing.

It is all very well to be a doctor and to do operations, prescribe treatment and deal with complicated midwifery, and it is a simple thing to order hot applications every two hours, blanket baths and frequent irrigations, but it is a different matter to have to do all these things yourself or even to supervise them.

A doctor is not a nurse, and I found it very uphill work. Furthermore, not only was I a physician, surgeon and gynecologist, as well as nurse-in-charge of the hospital, but also builder, detective, judge and settler of family disputes. In the middle of all this I had to sit for a language examination.

Night and day there was work to be done, and, above all, the African staff to be watched and guided at every turn. Always I had the feeling that directly I left the hospital the staff heaved a sigh and said: "There goes the Bwana. Now we can have a breather!"

There are, of course, notable exceptions who have a sense of responsibility. Old Sechelela, the Matron, was a grand person and wholly to be trusted. Her keen sense of humor took the edge off many a difficult situation. Her daughter and granddaughter were both trained midwives. The latter, Mwendwa, was most capable, for all her four feet ten inches. Many times she has sat beside a patient the whole twenty-four hours because she felt the case needed her.

Some of the nurses were heroic at times. One of our trained girls, Blandina, had only her right eye; the left was ruined by a witch doctor. She had two children, and was expecting a third. She did her job as ward sister till noon, went home and cooked for her family, and at three o'clock informed me she wanted to be admitted to the hospital. I saw her carrying a kerosene tin filled with hot, sterile water which she had personally prepared for her own use. I did my evening round of the hospital at seven. All was quiet. At eight o'clock she was receiving my congratulations, and I said all the right things as I admired her eight-pound daughter!

For a change, I spent the whole of that night in bed, blissfully unconscious of what was going on at the hospital.

At two a.m. another case came in. The junior girl was in a predicament: her senior had fever. Should she leave the patient and call me, or should she do the whole thing herself? Blandina awoke, and, seeing the state of affairs, got up and conducted the case; cleaned up and bathed the baby before she went to bed — and all that within eight hours of the arrival of her own infant! When I was told about it all next morning, Blandina sat up in bed, and dismissed the whole affair with a gesture:

"But what else could I do, Bwana? The night nurse on duty had malaria, and the junior girl has not had enough experience. Nothing else could have been done."

In those days, my grip of the language was insecure, and I gave some remarkable orders. Blandina was almost ready to go home. She was walking about the ward as I did my round. I was speaking to one woman when a patient, three beds away, sat up, leaned over the side of the bed, and noisily but accurately spat in the corner. I turned round to the junior nurse:

"Gwe yinojeye uwalonjere wacekulu wose welece kufunya mate mu muhuzi."

Blandina put her hand over her mouth, and doubled up with mirth.

"Blandina," I said, "it is bad for discipline for you to do that. Stop laughing. This matter's serious."

"But, Bwana, you don't know what you said. You told her that the women must not spit in the gravy!"

"I didn't," I said. "I said that they mustn't spit in the corner."

"Bwana, you said *muhuzi,* and that means gravy. You should have said *nhuzi.*"

I supervised everything I could, but felt that the dressings might safely be left to a senior girl. One morning, however, a child with a big ulcer complained of an itch. She was always making a fuss, so I was firm, and went on to the next case — an old woman with an infected elbow joint produced by a thorn and a manure compress. I did her dressing, a foul, stinking job, and as I went to scrub my hands, the small lady with the ulcer said, aggrievedly:

"You'd be itchy, too, Bwana, if you had these in your ulcer!" And she held up an exhibit, a fat maggot, between finger and thumb!

The outer dressing only had been changed, and the flies had made the most of their opportunity.

I sneezed fourteen times. Daudi solemnly counted them. At the end of my marathon I wiped my eyes, and said:

"*Yah,* this sounds grim. I shall have asthma before the day's out. You'd better fix up the lamp with red cellophane."

I sneezed violently as I tried to listen to a chest. I almost broke a needle in an unfortunate malarial patient as I repeated the performance while giving an injection. I left Daudi to open two abscesses and remove a large thorn, while I sneezed helplessly in the sterilizing room.

With my morning tea came a pile of six clean handkerchiefs. I gulped down two cups, between sneezes, and then I felt an ominous tightness in my chest. It seemed as though a giant had put a broad strap round my ribs, and was pulling it tight.

"Daudi," I said, "the worst has happened. I am getting another attack of asthma. Tell Yohanna to get the barrow ready."

Daudi grinned.

At lunch time I found the gardener at the ward door with a rusty barrow, fitted out in luxury style with two ancient cushions.

"*Ghari,* Bwana," smiled he.

We stopped at the dispensary, where Daudi was waiting with a pill and a glass of water. I swallowed it down, and Yohanna wheeled me rapidly home, and, as Daudi told me afterwards, the sound of my sneezing became less and less as the distance between us became greater and greater!

An urgent operation case kept my thoughts off myself. I sat on a high stool to operate, and twice during the proceedings I was given an injection to maintain my ability to breathe. Fortunately the sneezing had subsided!

At sun-down I made a complete round of the hospital, and returned home in my one-wheel chariot, feeling that all was comparatively well. Timothy hung out the red lamp which meant that if I was called, the barrow must be brought to transport me.

It was eleven o'clock. I was sitting up in bed, surrounded by every pillow our jungle house boasted, when I heard the ominous squeak of the barrow.

"Bwana," said a voice. "Are you awake?"

"Yes," I panted. "I am."

"There's trouble in the children's ward."

At that moment a hyena howled. It seemed only a few yards away. The messenger jumped.

"*Yah!* That one was close."

I was still thinking of hyenas, when the barrow rattled through the hospital gate and I was deposited outside the children's ward. As I alighted, I stumbled, but Mwendwa, Daudi's wife, put a large arm round me, and steered me up the steps. She smiled in the lamplight.

"*Yah!* Bwana. You've grown old in a night. It is not the children's ward you require!"

"No, indeed!" I panted. "It's the old men's home."

She laughed, and brought me into the ward, to a scene of indescribable chaos. Three old women, who were relatives of a small boy, the proud possessor of an ulcer the size of a saucer, were crowded around a lamp in the middle of the floor, holding down the shrieking child. They had removed the bandages to see if we were using the right treatment!

"Bwana," said Mwendwa, "they hid inside the fence, and then crept into the ward. I went to get another blanket for little Yusufu, and when I came back, behold, this is what I found. They refuse to go."

Now, I didn't mean to look fierce, but I was trying my best to hold back a string of sneezes which I felt were in the championship class. The old women got to their feet, and backed away. They were not used to the furnishings of the ward, and one of them tripped and nearly fell over a stool. The sneezes were getting the better of me. I moved my head back, and sneezed with great violence. I will admit I put more than was necessary into the effort! With gasps of alarm, the old women rushed through the door, and I nearly choked in an effort to sort out my laughter from the pressing desire to follow up my first triumph! Mwendwa was weak with laughing. She dressed the child's sore and gave him a dose of quietening medicine. I looked around the ward. The children had settled down to sleep again, and all was quiet.

I felt sleep was an absolute necessity, when the door burst open over the way, and the voice of the nurse in charge of the maternity ward said:

"Quick! Get the Bwana at once!"

Mwendwa helped me across. It was four o'clock before that job was done, and I returned home, too tired to sleep. Pills and injections kept me on my feet the next day. Case after case came in that just had to be dealt with, and in the afternoon a high Government official paid me a visit. I sank back in my chair with a groan as the car disappeared over the plains, and almost at once was asleep. Then I realized Samson was at the door.

"Bwana, Bwana!"

"Yes, Samson. What's up?"

"There's a man out here. He wants to see you."

"Oh, I can't see him, Samson. I'm tired."

"But, Bwana, he's in the middle of a fit, and is unconscious!"

I was out of the door in a moment, and used a clothespin to force apart the rigid jaws of the unfortunate. His lips were slate-blue in color. I tilted his head back, and pushed his chin forward. He drew in a gasping breath, and I knew all was well. Some lads brought a stretcher and he was carried up to the hospital.

Daudi stayed behind for a moment.

"He has been drinking, Daudi, and I think he's got epilepsy."

"Truly, Bwana, but he has been drinking *nghangala* — native mead — brewed from honey."

I left instructions for his treatment, and he was carried off to the ward. Timothy called me to dinner, and the next thing I remember was someone shaking me by the shoulder.

"Bwana, wake up, Bwana!"

I lifted my head sleepily, and saw in front of me, my dinner — stone cold. I had gone to sleep after eating but a few mouthfuls. Somehow I finished that meal, but before I could get to bed there came an urgent call. Our epileptic patient had taken a turn for the worse. Hour after hour we battled for his life. I felt I couldn't carry on another minute, and just prayed for strength. Just before dawn he died. I went home, had a shower, and put on my clothes again for another day's work that lay ahead. I had had one hour's sleep in forty-eight. Fortunately the asthma was at bay, and I realized that these things had to crop up sometimes when there is only one doctor for over twenty-five thousand people. Mechanically I followed that day's routine. At sun-down, I stumbled into bed, and at once was asleep. It was ten o'clock the next morning when I awoke, realizing something was wrong. My left eye refused to shut. My mouth drooped and saliva insisted upon trickling out of the corner. I tried without success to straighten out my features. Timothy brought me tea and toast, but the food tasted like cotton-wool. I walked up to the hospital, but evidently looked so wretched that Daudi took one look at me, and led me home again, and said:

"Go to bed, Bwana. I shall run the hospital, and when any difficulties arise, will consult you down here." And just before he went back to the job we prayed together.

"Daudi," I said, "you've got a big job."

"Yes, Bwana."

"And here's a verse for you. A verse that'll help, whatever the problem may be: 'I can do all things through Christ, Who strengtheneth me.' "

For the best part of a week that trained African lad ran the hospital on his own, while I lay in bed and felt like the man in *Punch* who said he wouldn't mind insomnia if only he could get a bit of sleep! Each evening Daudi came to report his doings. Together we went over each case and its treatment. I was amazed to see the grip my African lieutenant had of the principles of medicine. This is the sort of conversation you would have heard.

"Bwana, there is old Majimbe, wife of Cikoti, she came in very hot, temperature one hundred and four. Kefa did her blood slide, which was very full of malaria wogs. So, Bwana, I injected five grains of quinine and gave the usual medicines and diet."

"But what about the relatives, Daudi, didn't they object to your doing these things?"

Daudi smiled.

"Behold, Bwana. I told them she would die without our help. I showed them the bloodslide and they agreed to the treatment."

Another case record went like this:

"How's the baby with the infected eyes, Daudi?"

"Better, Bwana. I gave argyrol drops and irrigations as directed."

"And the old man with pneumonia?"

"He is worse, Bwana, you'll need to operate, but he won't be ready for four or five days."

"How do you know?"

"Didn't you say last time that there must be thickening in the chest fluids before you can do the operation?"

"Yes, but how do you know the fluids weren't thick?"

"*Yah!* Bwana, that was easy. I took some off with a needle and syringe."

Nurses and Helpers

STAFF AND BABIES

The hospital staff with one week's new-born babies — fourteen of them!

"Eehoo! Bwana. Babies, babies, babies, and babies — sixty-two this month so far, and still five days to go."

"Well, Sech, we've dealt with eight hundred babies this year, and seven years ago the women wouldn't even come near the hospital."

"They come now, Bwana, only because you and the Wabibi — the Sisters — speak our language and understand our customs." (Babies)

A SMILING GROUP OF TRAINED AFRICAN NURSES

"We are building for the future, and can expect big things when the present generation are grandmothers." (Staff)

NURSES CARRYING HOSPITAL STORES

At the end of each briefing he would go back to the hospital and carry on. My only task was to sit up in bed with a strip of adhesive plaster holding up the angle of my mouth. From this vantage point I examined such patients as Daudi found too much for him. The people were escorted into my bedroom by the cook boy, each of them clutching a note. One such note, written on the back of a soap wrapper, said:

> Dear Bwana,
>
> Here's a chap who walked forty miles. Has pains in the back, and perhaps ulcers inside — and (in brackets) — he smells rather!

These notes brightened up my days in bed considerably.

"L's" and "R's" are interchangeable in Chigogo, so I was not surprised when another note came:

> Bwana,
>
> Have just admitted a man with abscess on his river.

Rest, sundry medications, and a hot-water bottle had the desired effect, and, although I had a lop-sided look, I could deal with the job. While I was away the staff had done everything that could be asked of them. They were on their mettle, and I could not find fault with their wards or their work, but when they saw me back on the job, they felt it was an indication to relax.

Phoebe was the nurse looking after the women's ward. On my morning round I found the cupboards in a horrible mess, soiled linen hidden away in them, and dirty instruments covered up in a corner.

Then I found that she hadn't given out the medicines, and I issued a solemn warning.

"Bwana," said some of the patients, "she has not sponged us, nor made our beds, nor given us our medicines. Behold, she just goes and sits beside the fire."

"Yes," added a girl in the corner, "and she wraps herself in *my* blanket, because she says it's cold."

"*Kah,*" said Sechelela, "the Bwana knows a means of keeping people warm other than by using blankets!"

Phoebe promised solemnly that it would not occur again, but next morning, when I arrived at the hospital, I was greeted by a storm of protest from the women's ward.

"No medicines this morning, Bwana."

"My bed is uncomfortable."

"She's taken my blanket again."

I pacified them, and set out to find Phoebe. There she was, in the same old place, sitting in front of the fire, wrapped in the same blanket, peacefully dreaming as she watched the flames curl round the clay cooking pot.

"Phoebe," I said. "What are you doing?"

"*O-o-o-o-o-o,* nothing, Bwana."

"Obviously," I said. "Come with me."

In an extremely ferocious voice, I gave her pointed instructions. She did her work, and did it well, and my final word was:

"Don't let this happen again tomorrow."

I must admit I was surprised when I heard the same round of complaints from the women's ward. It was an identical state of affairs. No medicines; absolutely nothing had been done.

I have always been fond of Gilbert and Sullivan, and I feel that anyone undertaking a "Jungle Doctor's" job would be advised to study the works of those eminent men!

Daudi heard me whistling, rather inaccurately, fragments from *The Mikado.*

"*He-e-e-e-e-e,*" said he. "Be careful, the Bwana is whistling his battle song!"

"*Yah!*" said Samson. "Behold that smile upon his face. Trouble is near for someone."

"Samson," I said, "call the staff. Tell them to assemble in the women's ward."

"Yes, Bwana."

"*He-e-e-e-e,*" said Samson, "behold, the trouble is not mine."

"What," said Daudi, "is your conscience uneasy?"

Samson shook his head vigorously, and I laughed. "Not you, this time; it's Phoebe again."

"*Kah,*" said Daudi, "truly she is the pain in the neck."

I went off to the women's kitchen, still whistling, and there was Phoebe, sitting looking into the fire, with her shoulders covered with the same blanket.

"*Mbukwa* — Good morning," I said.

"*Mbukwa* — Good morning, Bwana."

"*Uli muswanu* — Are you well?" I asked.

"*Nili muswanu du* — Yes, I am all right."

"*Ukuliaci?* — What do you eat?" I asked.

"*Wugali du* — Only porridge," she replied.

I went on right through the full list of Gogo greetings, and then said:

"Will you come to the ward?"

Now, an African doesn't mind if you storm at him. He expects that, but he doesn't like quietness, and he positively fears ridicule.

The staff stood at attention as we walked into the ward. The patients sat up expectantly. Sechelela came out to the front when I called her.

"Sech," I said, "for three days this girl has not looked after her patients properly. She said it was cold, so she sat near the fire."

"Bwana," said the old African woman, "that is our custom. We leave the sick with a gourd of water, and go ourselves to keep warm."

"But," I said, "do we follow heathen custom here?"

"No, Bwana," she said, "we follow in the steps of our Master, Jesus Christ."

So I explained to the staff what we expected of them as Christian Africans. I agreed that we would all make mistakes, but I felt, in this case, Phoebe's memory needed a little help. Three times she had been warned, and three times she had forgotten.

"Behold," I said, "this is my medicine for failing memories."

All the staff sat solemnly round and watched her discomfort.

"Get the ward book, Phoebe."

The book was produced. I turned to the first bed.

"What should this patient have? What medicine?"

"Zinc eyedrops, Bwana. Three drops into each eye."

"Right!" I said. "Sit on that stool, Phoebe. Sechelela, put drops into her eyes."

"*He-e-e-e-e-e!*" said Phoebe.

"Be quiet!" I said. "Do as you're told!"

There was a gasp from the nurse as the drops found their targets!

"And now this case. What does she have?"

"Mag. sulp., Bwana. Two aspirin tablets, and her chest is rubbed."

"Esther," said I, turning to a notoriously heavy-handed girl, "rub Phoebe's chest. Sechelela, give her the Epsom salts and the aspirin."

Phoebe opened her mouth to protest, and Sechelela made the most of the opportunity.

The next patient had a hot application put on the back of her neck.

The next had drops put in her ears.

At the far end of the ward a mustard plaster needed to be applied.

Within the next twenty minutes Phoebe had experienced most of the common treatments in medicine.

With a sigh, she turned to me:

"*E-e-e-e-e,* Bwana. Can I ever forget? *Yah,* this mustard planter's burning me. *He-e-e-e-e-e,* my poor stomach."

The staff could contain themselves no longer. They rocked with laughter. Tears were streaming down Daudi's face.

"*He-e-e-e-e*, Bwana, that's better treatment than many whacks from a very thick stick."

Even I thought that Phoebe was cured, and she was — for three weeks. Then, one Thursday, when we make a determined onslaught upon any new arrivals from the insect world that find their way into the hospital beds, *via* the visitors, Phoebe sat down, and said:

"I refuse to de-bug beds today."

She had no particular reason. She just wouldn't do it. It was useless reading the Riot Act, so I whistled cheerily *The Mikado* again, and called the staff.

They all arrived expectantly.

"My children," I said, "I need your help. Phoebe will not deal with the insects in her ward today. I want volunteers to do this work for her, with me."

Everybody stepped forward a pace.

"*Kah!*" said Daudi. "Has she not learned yet? Does she not know the danger of that little song that the Bwana whistles?"

We lighted a plumber's blowtorch. Insecticide sprays were brought. With kerosene-tinfuls of water boiled, and with extreme cheerfulness, the staff set to work to deal with the invaders.

I whispered one instruction to my helpers:

"Don't touch the bed in the corner."

Phoebe sat comfortably in the sun, watching proceedings.

"Bwana," she said, pointing with her chin, "You haven't done the bed in the corner."

I agreed. We hadn't.

"Bwana,' she said again. "You haven't done that bed in the corner."

"No," I said, "we haven't."

"Why?" she asked. "Why haven't you done it?"

"Oh," I said, "because that's your bed."

"My bed? Oh, no! My bed is over there." Her chin was directed towards the nurses' quarters.

"No," I said, "that *was* your bed, but this is now your bed."

"*He-e-e-e-e-e,*" she said, "but will I not be bitten?"

"Will you not?" I said, with emphasis.

"But, Bwana, I can't sleep there. I could not sleep on a bed like that."

"And what of your patients?" I asked. "Would they not have had difficulty in sleeping?"

"Oh, that's different. They're sick."

Daudi chuckled.

"Don't worry, Phoebe. You sleep in that bed, and before long, you, too, will be sick."

The unfortunate girl put her head in her hands and groaned.

We left her. The treatment was carried out to the letter. At the end of a week she came to me and said:

"Bwana, many messengers have helped my memory these nights."

I sat with a very straight face, and recorded these details for future reference.

One needs the wisdom of Solomon and the patience of Job in training Africans. One cannot drag people from the Stone Age into the twentieth century in a few short months.

I had started lessons again, and was on the way to the hospital with books under each arm, when I noticed a girl of about sixteen years or so sitting under a tree, with literally thousands of flies on and about her. With difficulty, I got her story. She was an epileptic, and her family believed she was bewitched. About a month previously she had had a fit, and, since no Mugogo will touch a person in this state, she was left lying with her arm in the fire till the seizure was over. By that time her arm was charred to the bone. The local medicine man did not help matters much with a poultice made from goat's fat. She drew aside an unspeakably dirty cloth. What had once been a hand was now a crawling mass hanging by a dried-up tendon, while the bones of the forearm stuck out forlornly. The odor was terrific. It nearly made Daudi ill, and that is saying a lot! We had no choice but to amputate, and, after a successful operation, we trained her to do useful handicraft with the remaining member before sending her home.

One morning came tragedy in our makeshift operating room. I fought for the life of a little chap, aged twelve, who had been terribly mauled by a baboon. For eight hours he had tossed on a dirty goat's skin in the smoky gloom of a mud hut, and had suffered unspeakable things at the hands of the witch doctor. A crude hammock slung on a thornbush pole had been his ambulance for eight miles over the plains.

African nurses and dispensers hurried here and there, boiling up instruments in kerosene tins, bringing sterilized dressings and feverishly pumping up battered primuses. We battled all that morning to save the little fellow's life. How I longed for the everyday conveniences of a hospital at home, the oxygen and the facilities for immediate blood transfusion; but none of those things were available here. In the middle of the job came in Sechelela.

"Bwana," she panted, "there's a woman" — here followed a vivid description of a dangerous obstetrical complication.

As I operated I gave instructions how it was to be dealt with. The old African nurse stayed only long enough to repeat my instructions and then hurried away.

At last the operation was over and I hurried to the maternity ward where all was under control. I spent the afternoon in the men's ward giving the little boy fluids from a dilapidated thermos flask by means of rubber tubes, connected together with eye-droppers.

At midnight I was called. Opening the ward door I stumbled over the sleeping form of a relative of one of my small patients who had elected to sleep near the doorway. The hurricane lantern at the other end of the room was before my operation case, the anxious night nurse was bending over him. In a minute my fingers were on his pulse. It gradually became weaker and weaker; then it fluttered, revived a little, fluttered again, and was gone!

Gently I pulled the unbleached calico sheet over his head, and sat disconsolately by the bed. I should have been able to save him. Could I have done anything more? On the night air came the thumpa-thump of the drums, the weird chant of dancers, the howling of jackals. I groaned! To think that this had been going on for years, and I had been sitting complacently at home, feeling that I was doing a grand thing in giving five pounds a year to foreign missions! I thought of the needless things I had bought, not realizing that ten shillings actually means a saved life. I wished I had given ten times the amount, but now I could do nothing more about it. I was the unfortunate in the front line who had to watch suffering and death stalk through the land almost unchecked.

The door opened again. I heard the relatives whispering as they took the little lad away to his last resting place, and I tried to shut from my ears the weeping of the broken-hearted mother.

Things had a way of becoming hectic, and then settling down to a steady routine.

The whole countryside had been brown, dry and incredibly dusty! The sun was scorchingly hot as we panted about the hospital. Everybody seemed limp, and tempers were very near the surface. Patients complained, the staff broke ten thermometers in a week, donkeys ate part of the grass roof, and white ants followed their example in the dispensary. Five babies chose to arrive all in one night.

Then suddenly the rain came. Everything "greened-up" at an incredible rate. Cases that had not responded to treatment suddenly took a change for the better. Everyone cheered up, and — best of all — a fresh Sister arrived.

Sechelela, Daudi and I met outside the native kitchen and simply thanked God for His help through most difficult days. It had been hard, but it had had its brighter moments.

CHAPTER 15

Christmas Day

IT WAS Christmas Eve. All were in their oldest clothes. The hospital ironing room was in great demand. It was nothing more or less than a wattle-and-daub structure, furnished with a rickety table, obviously made from gasoline cases.

One of the strangest queues that I have ever seen waited their turn for their Christmas ironing. It consisted of carefully rolled shorts and shirts, and other weird garments, placed in a line by the owners, some of whom had blankets wrapped round them, others in the oldest and most decrepit of shorts, and still others with a minimum of ragged cloth appropriately draped. I think the lad who amused me most had his back to me, and was making an impassioned speech on something or other. He was dressed very inadequately in an apron that had once belonged to my wife!

"Hello, everybody," I said. "What are you up to?"

"Christmas tomorrow, Bwana. We've got to look our best. We are ironing our clothes. Behold, it is our Savior's birthday. We want to look our best to honor Him."

"Good work," I replied.

A grinning face peered at me from inside the ironing room. Samson came out of the door, and blew a cloud of white ashes from the inside of the charcoal iron. This he swung in the air until the red coals inside it glowed. He put one horny finger on to the ironing surface, and withdrew it quickly, apparently satisfied!

"Bwana," called a voice from the ward nearby. "Ready!"

I walked in to find Daudi had rigged up for me a special contraption consisting of a thermos flask, some thin glass tubing, a hypodermic needle and some rubber. Our patient was a pathetic-looking little girl, lying inert in a brightly painted little cot. Daudi lowered the side of this. I smiled at my patient.

"It won't hurt, Nzuga, and this medicine will make you stronger."

She smiled wanly, and said:

"Bwana, a little bit more pain doesn't matter. *Kah!* how I suffered at home."

She had had a severe bout of tropical dysentery, and but for the visit of one of our African clergy to her home in the bush, miles away, she would undoubtedly have died. The old man had wrapped the child in his own blanket, and seated her on the saddle of his bicycle, and wheeled her twenty miles to our hospital. As I had seen them arrive, the elderly African almost dropping from fatigue, his little charge nearly unconscious, I felt somehow it was a modern version of the story Jesus told of the Good Samaritan.

As I watched two buxom nurses carrying their little patient gently to the hospital ward, I said to the old man who had made the first step in saving her life:

"Well, Mika, was it not very tiring?"

He smiled, and pointed to a picture on the wall. It was a print of our Savior on the Cross: the same picture that, over a century ago, had gripped a nobleman; and, underneath it, in Chigogo, was written: "All this I did for thee. What hast thou done for Me?"

"Bwana," he said. "It was just one way in which I could thank Him."

For a month the little girl had hung between life and death. The issue was still in the balance, but somehow I felt she would recover. As I injected into her veins the solution which would build her up, I watched the nurses decorating the ward. The nearest approach we could manage to holly was a pepper tree. In each corner of the room, planted in a kerosene tin, was a huge sunflower. Long paper streamers were draped above the windows and from the rafters. They were obviously cut from newspaper gummed together and then stained with very diluted red ink and purple, green and blue stains from the laboratory.

Elisha, the carpenter, called "*Hodi*" outside the door, and with an accompaniment of grunts and groans carried in a red geranium in what, six months before, had been a hand basin in the operating room. This may sound imposing, but it was merely half a kerosene tin. I watched the flow of liquid. Suddenly it stopped. I arranged tubes and needles and once again it started.

My little patient was watching everything with the greatest interest. A smile came over her face.

"Bwana, isn't it lovely? Look at the flowers!"

Daudi was busy blowing up three football bladders which he had duly illustrated. Two big black eyes and a vast mouth surmounted each of them. Nzuga laughed.

"Why do all this, Bwana?"

I refilled the thermos before answering, and then sat down, and told her that years and years ago, in a stable, a Baby Boy had been born.

"A European, Bwana?"

"No," I replied, "He wasn't! He lived not far from Africa. He wasn't either a European or an African. He was the link between us. When He was born, His mother wrapped Him up in a cloth, and put Him in the hay in the box where the cows got their food. That little Baby, born in such a humble way, was God's own Son."

"*Yah,*" said the little girl. "Is this true?"

"Every word. Listen. That night, when the sun had set, there were shepherds looking after their sheep in the jungle, and they heard voices singing, and telling them of the birth of the Son of God, and then they saw angels. A little later three chiefs from far away arrived bringing presents. They had followed a star which led them to the very place where the Baby was lying."

"But Bwana, didn't they wonder that the Son of God should be born in a stable?"

"They did, indeed. But they knew that God knows best. That was the first Christmas Day — the Birthday of the Lord Jesus Christ."

At that moment, one of the nurses in a very tuneful voice, started to sing "The First Noel." My little patient listened, entranced. As she listened, the last of the medicine ran into her system. I removed the needle, and bandaged up her arm. Another nurse arrived with a dose of medicine. The little mite swallowed it down and said:

"Bwana, I would like to have seen Jesus."

"Yes," I said. "So would I. But what I do like about Him is that we can talk to Him any time, anywhere." And I explained to her how the Son of God was living, and how, while He was yet a young Man, He had been condemned and had died willingly, so that we might know God.

Tears filled her eyes, and she said: "Bwana, will you talk to Him now?"

The nurse got down from the table where she had been working with the decorations. Daudi put down the instrument that he was about to sterilize, and we knelt round the cot and in their own language I thanked God for sending a Savior to the world, to be born as we were born, to live as we live, to experience things as we experience things, and to die that we might live.

Christmas Day itself was to be a tremendous affair. A bag of rice was in the store. Daudi had dug a trench in which fires would be lighted tomorrow to cook great pots of goat's stew. Even at that moment Samson, who had finished his ironing successfully, was sawing up great blocks of sticky brown sugar with a hacksaw.

Two hours before dawn I woke to the sound of the schoolgirls, half a mile away, singing "Christmas Awake." I smiled, and promptly went to sleep again!

Santa Claus had made his annual trip to Tanganyika on time. My small son had a bulging stocking. He descended upon my bed at the first sign of dawn, and we had just got to the stage of investigating some most interesting-looking sweets, stickily wrapped in cellophane, when Daudi appeared at the door with a parcel.

"Bwana, this is from the hospital."

There was a cleverly-plaited leather belt for me, and one of patterned beadwork for my wife. For David there was a carved lion, and for the baby a wooden ring, which, Daudi informed me professionally, he had sterilized, and would it not be useful to help her teeth find their way into view? I thanked him, and then found the whole staff at the door. Daudi waved his hand, and they proceeded to sing a selection of Christmas carols. How long this would have gone on I do not know. Suddenly Sechelela appeared.

"Quick, Bwana, quick! The teacher from Kirtinku has arrived. I think he has gone mad. He does not talk sense. He waves his hands and groans horribly. I told him it was Christmas, and to behave himself, but he picked up a stick, and behold, here I am."

I got dressed, and was half-way to the hospital, when I was presented with a document, hastily written on the back of a soap packet. I read it, and laughed till the tears streamed down my face.

"*Yah,*" said Sech. "Bwana, do not laugh, he is mad all right. Poor man! And his wife such a nice woman, and his children are at the school. *Kah!*"

Daudi was reading the letter. He, too, burst out laughing. So I let everybody into the secret. The teacher had been visiting relatives for the Christmas season. They had been singing far into the night. He had been quite well till midnight, and at this hour he had yawned. In the middle of his yawn he felt as though his jaw had been grasped in a clamp. The letter said pains shot up the sides of his face, and he had lost his ability to speak clearly. He had rushed through the night, fifteen miles to us, and behold, everyone thought he was mad!

"Listen," I said. "This poor man has dislocated his jaw. It will not be five minutes' work to fix it up again."

He sat on the hospital veranda in the early light of a Tanganyikan Christmas Day. I put my thumbs into his mouth beside his jaw bone, lifted slightly, and pushed. There was a click, and a sigh of satisfaction from both surgeon and patient.

"*Yah,*" said the teacher. "*Swanu* — good. Oh, thank you, Bwana."

The staff clapped, and Daudi said:

"Stay to our party."

It was a day of great joy. No one received expensive presents. Christmas dinner was goat's stew and rice, with brown sugar to follow. But there was a spirit of Christmas, a knowledge that Jesus Christ, who was God and Man, was with us. Nzuga, looking better than I had seen her, clung to a pencil and a minute doll.

"Behold, Bwana," said she. "Wasn't Jesus good to me?"

I nodded, and said, "*Cawalamusa* — good night," to her; I listened to the strains of the staff and convalescent patients singing "Holy Night," as I walked home in the starlight.

CHAPTER 16

The Wet Season

WEATHER prophets would not make much of a living in Tanganyika, although umbrella merchants do very well indeed. Rains run to schedule, and, unless you fear the sun, you can safely leave your umbrella in mothballs from April 30th till November 15th. Even though you may see banks of heavy black clouds in the sky, you can be secure in the knowledge that the rain will not fall out of season.

All through the dry weather, the baobabs had the appearance of great, gaunt, up-ended turnips; the countryside was brown and burnt and inexpressibly drab; whirlwinds hundreds of feet high swept the bare plains.

One afternoon I noticed buds on the baobabs, and by evening great velvety, white flowers had appeared. In the moonlight these looked like the silver trappings of some giant Christmas tree. The leaves started to sprout, and within two weeks the great trees were covered with a deep green foliage.

"Behold! The baobabs know the rains are here!" said the people, and a few days later, just before sunset, came vivid forked lightning, followed by distant rumblings of thunder. The air was suddenly cool, and you could smell the good, moist earth. We scurried to shutter the windows. Then it came. Solid sheets of fiercely wind-driven rain, ushered in by huge drops that sounded like pebbles rattling on the tin roof. In an hour or so, however, it was all over.

The next day showed great damage to the face of the country. Erosion channels had appeared in the night, where tons of soil had been washed out. Within twenty-four hours there were signs of tiny shoots underfoot, and in a week the dry, brown hills were a deep green. In this season the Wagogo go to their gardens and work from dawn till dark; while the unfortunate who has to travel by car at this time of the year gets out his chains, the shovels, the hoe, a great roll of rope, and provides himself with a few shillings' worth of cents threaded on a piece of string, in case he needs to be dragged out of bogs or rivers by man-power.

You cannot trust the weather for an hour. One day the Padre was called to Dodoma. In spite of black clouds over the hills, there seemed to be every chance of a dry safari. Three miles out he was bogged — not badly, but just long enough to let the storm break and for rivers to come rushing down on him. For two solid hours it pelted down.

I was keeping a watchful eye on a complicated midwifery case, and, standing at the window, I watched river after river rush down and turn the road to soft, sticky, red mud.

"Bwana had good luck today, Sechelela," I said to the old matron. "He will have fun in that mud with his rotten old car."

At that moment a perspiring native, dressed in a loin-cloth and carrying a one-and-sixpenny umbrella, came up and thrust a dirty note into my hand. I unfolded it and read:

> Dear Doc: We are sitting in the middle of a lake. We got stuck just past Cipoko, where that ditch cuts across the road. The car is supported on stones, with one wheel hanging over a precipice. If you could bring some timber it would help, also if you could muster the lads of the village with a rope.

I translated this into Chigogo, and even the patient laughed. A few instructions in Sechelela's ear, an injection to give my patient rest, and I rushed off to collect twenty stalwarts and a thirty-foot rope and some timber, and away we went.

The first river we came to was a roaring, muddy torrent six feet deep, and running very swiftly. I dived in and swam vigorously, and with all my strength; even then I was carried fifty yards down stream before I managed to scramble up the opposite bank. Few Wagogo can swim, so we threw over a rope, and, one by one, dragged them across. Two hundred yards further along a fairly shallow river rushed down between muddy banks that were inexpressibly slippery. All got over safely, although one bold spirit who scorned the rope was swept down stream and nearly drowned. I dived in and hauled him out. Another fifty yards and we came to another torrent, which gave us some difficulty. We crossed three more rivers, and were a most bedraggled collection when we reached Forsgate.

He was cheerfully making the best of things, with one front wheel over a precipice and the other dangling over a four-foot waterfall. The front axle was supported by a pile of stones. It was impossible to hear a word spoken for the roar of the water, and every few minutes great pieces of the bank, eaten out by the flood waters, would crash into the swirling eddies beside the car.

A rope was tied to the back axle, and a dozen men pulled while the rest contrived footholds and put their shoulders under the front wheels. Forsgate blew the horn. One tremendous heave, and boards were slipped under the wheels; another, and the car skidded back into safety. The lads of the village, cheering vigorously, pushed the car round the soft mud, and proceeded to tow her home in triumph. They cheered again as they received a handsome tip of fifteen cents each.

As the countryside becomes vividly green, the light seems to change and become mellowed with a curious green tinge. It rains frequently, often an inch at a time, and the gardens grow apace. No Mugogo will get out his hoe until the rains come.

"*Kulima hakavu?* — To cultivate hard soil? Oh, no!" they laugh. "That is not our custom."

Gardens of maize and millet spring up all over the place. Caterpillars arrive by the thousands, but so also do flocks of ibis, which the Wagogo call *yobwa*. These birds migrate from northern European swamps. Coming in large numbers, they effectively deal with all the insects. No Mugogo would ever dream of harming one.

The wise among the people rotate their crops with peanuts and sweet-potatoes, or nourish the ground by digging in beans. The unwise ones tear the heart out of the garden, then leave it to clear another out of the virgin forest.

Should it not rain, the people are faced with disaster, for this means drought, and drought means famine. Naturally, the prospect perturbs them greatly, and at once they enlist the help of the professional rain-maker.

There was an old racketeer named Chelube, whose technique was to get a black bull and set it in the middle of a crowd of Wagogo, who then proceeded to dance around it, making a fiendish row from dawn till dusk. A few preselected dancers had special functions. Some were to dance in the inner circle and crawl under the bull every now and then, while others poured water over the long-suffering creature. Chelube sat apart, muttering incantations, and collected six cows for a day's work.

One year there was a particularly severe drought. Chelube was called in, and sat muttering furiously. The Wagogo danced feverishly, while the bull was subjected to extra indignities; but nothing happened. A deputation was sent to bring in Chelube and give him a beating, but the wily old rain-maker had already fled, with all his cattle.

No less than thirty-six inches of rain fell in one wet season, and it seemed absurd ever to have called Ugogo a desert. The countryside was a mass of flowers; acres of white, bell-like blooms with purple centers, tall native hollyhocks of lemon and purple, yellow daisies, and little dark red clover-like flowers growing in the feathery grass. The trees were festooned with convolvulus in delicate shades of pink, purple and orange, while a smaller variety in white and pale yellow grew on the low shrubs. Some trees were covered entirely with the purple and blue blossoms. Umbrella-like thorn trees took on the appearance of huge floral sunshades. There was so much color, it almost hurt your eyes to look at it.

One year it was terribly hot, even hotter than usual in these sun-scorched plains. The whole sweep of countryside was burnt — drab — brown. November came, and everyone waited expectantly for rain. The old men would stand around at sundown and nod their heads wisely, saying:

"It'll rain in three days' time. We can feel it in our bones." But week after week went by. The baobabs flowered, and within a day the delicate white flowers were nothing but brown, scorched tassels, hanging from the gaunt limbs.

"Kumbe," said the old men, "the baobabs know the rains are near."

But it seemed that even the baobabs were at fault!

Day after day the sun blazed down from a cloudless sky. November passed. Early in December clouds banked up round the hill. Thunder rumbled ominously but there was no rain. My cook shook his head.

"The clouds are merely angry, Bwana. They growl and frown, but do not weep."

The baobabs were in full leaf. But their leaves lacked the usual sleek greenness. They were in striking contrast to the browns and reds of the arid countryside. Dust storms invaded the plains; great clouds of dust that roared their way along — tubular whirlwinds that could be seen everywhere. All the signs of the approaching rains were there, but not one drop fell.

The people became restive. You saw them in groups talking earnestly together, and over and over again you heard the grim word: *"Nzala* — Famine."

Christmas passed — the New Year came. The rains were two months late. Unless ten inches came, and came quickly, the crops would be an utter failure, and thousands would starve.

One day the chief came to visit the African clergyman. I was called into consultation with them.

"Bwana," said the chief, "we have sinned. We must ask God's forgiveness and His help. Can we have next Sunday as a day of repentance and prayer for rain?"

And so it was agreed. Messengers were sent all over the country to tell the C.M.S. Out-Schools and Bush Churches that Sunday was to be a day set apart to pray for forgiveness and for the vital rain.

Sunday dawned. I woke late. There was not a breath of wind. The sky was heavily overcast. We went to church, and the whole place was packed. The chief and his family, the sub-chief, the village head-man, all were there. The African pastor preached a fighting sermon:

"Do we go to another chief when we want judgment given in our tribal disputes? Do we not go to the chief of our own tribe?

"When a child wants food, or clothing, or protection, does he not go to his own father?

"In times past, did we not call on our dead relatives; and pour beer on their graves so that they would help us?

"Did we not have Chelube to make charms and mutter and dance to bring rain?

"Have not all these things been done this year by the heathen?

"Now let us turn to God. Those of you who have not given your lives to Him, and invited His Son to be Chief in your hearts, do it now. Then, and then only, have you a claim on God your Creator, and Jesus Christ, His Son, who wants to be your Savior. You must follow His way and obey His orders as He has written them in His Book. Then He will answer your prayers!"

There was a great hush over the church as we prayed. The people streamed home over the plains. They knew that already their prayer was answered. They had the evidence of it as the smell of moist earth was borne to them on the breeze. Within an hour, soft, gentle rain was falling, and three inches followed within three days.

"Surely," said Daudi to me, "our God is a God who answers. We were unwise not to ask before."

The flowers come towards the end of the rains, and so, generally, does the High Court, which blissfully subpenas you or your staff, and cheerfully keeps you away from the job for days, paying all expenses. Often, after a week or so has elapsed, you are told: "Oh, he's pleaded guilty. We don't require your evidence now."

I was subpenaed once in a murder case. A local sub-chief and his friends had been drinking hard. One of the party started a brawl, and the chief was whacked in the abdomen with a knobkerri. He immediately collapsed, and, although obviously in agony, nothing was done for him, since no one would get a cow to pay for his being carried to the hospital. Next day, in the early afternoon, he was brought in, dying. I operated, and found the abdomen full of blood, and a spleen torn apart. I was about to pour back some of the blood into his veins when he died. Again a life had been lost through the old, old story of beer and "perhaps tomorrow he'll be better."

When I drove into Dodoma to give evidence in this case we started before dawn, but were repeatedly bogged, twice skidded off the road, and once very narrowly escaped coming to grief completely. After waiting about all day, I was told I would not be required, since — as usual — the accused had pleaded guilty. At four p.m. we set out for home in the teeth of a storm, driving as fast as the slippery roads would allow. Suddenly a black cloud came down on the hills. Crossing a wide river, we saw a white-crested breaker bearing down on us; if we had been caught in that boiling mass of muddy water, the car would have been rolled downstream like a cork. We were within five miles of home at sundown when we attempted to cross a running river. It was not very deep, but we bogged. The river rose rapidly. We had to tie the car to a tree to make sure it was not swept away. Lying flat in a rushing torrent, jacking up the car and putting successive stones under the wheels is no gentle pastime. We were soaking wet and bitterly cold, and we were in lion country! At midnight, with the aid of thirty men, we got out, only to find the road farther on quite impassable. We walked the last two miles through thick, sticky mud by the light of smoky lanterns. My car boy remarked:

"I wish the Bwana Judge had been with us in that river."

I heartily agreed, and would willingly, that night, have added the High Court and all its works.

CHAPTER 17

Iringa Safari

FOR A WEEK I had been looking forward to a few days of tennis, and had gone to Dodoma with the comforting feeling that the family were having a splendid holiday in the cool of the Southern Highlands, and that there was nobody really ill at the hospital.

Mvumi is singularly congenial to a doctor in one respect — there is no telephone for thirty-five miles. But at Dodoma I found a wire from Iringa:

Come immediately — Our return imperative.

I imagined all sorts of catastrophes to the children, and, with a sigh, put my racket back in the press and went to see the transport people. I found my man, a collarless Indian, sitting at an elaborate desk in a poky little office, and almost completely surrounded with bags of onions.

"There is absolutely no room in the mail truck, Doctor. I am sorry, extremely."

There was an air of finality about this speech. However, I said: "Is there no room on top? Can you not squeeze me in somewhere?

He shook his head and spread his hands hopelessly:

"The road is very bad, and the Public Works Department will issue no permits."

There seemed no way out, so I went to see my friend and patient, Mooloo Jan Mohammed. He knows everything about the doings in Dodoma, and at once he had a solution. Off we went to the rice and oil mills of one of his *khoja* — his clan.

"Thank you, Doctor. We will set forth just at four p.m. approximately, or thereabouts, for Iringa, but I have no room whatsoever at all in the car for passengers or baggage. The car is filled. Much regrets, but unavoidable."

Such were the remarks of the truck owner. I had no need to plead my own cause; my companion burst into a flood of Gujerati, but the corpulent miller was smiling and apologetic; two of his best clients had the front seat, and it was not large enough for three.

"My promise cannot be expunged, Doctor. I regret my clients have the front seat. There is no other explanation."

I was determined to go, so I suggested riding on top of the rice.

"It is impossible, so inconvenient to your health and posture, sir."

I pooh-poohed this idea, and made myself an armchair of bagged rice, and thanked him for his goodness in taking me. He said words would not convey his shame in not offering me a suitable seat. However, an old inner tube, partly inflated, and the judicious use of a cushion, gave me a relatively comfortable ride.

Sharp at four o'clock we set out, driving through the granite-strewn plains of Ugogo. The rainy season was just beginning. Every baobab looked like an oak, and the hills were dark green with massed thornbush. On the skyline great boulders stood out from the tops of the hills. The truck bumped its way over dry riverbeds and the corrugated, unmade surface of the Cape to Cairo road. Twenty-five miles of the journey was marked by the signpost indicating the turnoff to Mvumi Hospital.

On each side of the road native crops were being planted; men and women were hoeing their gardens or planting maize, millet or sorghum. The Gogo is a friendly soul, and is always willing to stop work for a moment on any pretext. Women, pounding their grain before their square, squat mud houses, waved, and small boys hurried humpbacked cattle, goats and fat-tailed sheep out of our way and shouted a cheery "*Jambo,* Bwana."

The sun was setting as we drove down a mountain pass to Fufu, a wide flat with a series of shallow lagoons. The whole place teemed with waterfowl. Duck and knob-billed Egyptian geese flew quacking and honking overhead, a long flight of white egrets strung over the sky, the setting sun shining on their slowly-moving wings. Golden-crested cranes flew ponderously above us, giving their strange cry, which is like the lament of a prowling tomcat. Crows squawked and quarrelled on their way home.

The sunset rapidly merged into night. I lay back and watched the gnarled branches of baobabs and the sharp thorns of the umbrella tree pass a foot or two above my head. The stars twinkled into sight through the tangled limbs, and I picked out the Southern Cross. We were following its guiding finger and traveling due south.

A grinding of brakes, and we were at Cibogolo. Sixty miles had been covered. A mere hundred to go, and it was seven-thirty p.m., or "*saa moja na nusu* — hour one-and-a-half," as time is reckoned in East Africa.

"Will you not be my guest, Doctor, for a cup of tea, please?" said one of the Indian merchants.

I got up from my rice-bag armchair, and scrambled down the side of the truck. We walked together to the "Hoteli," surely as strange a hotel as you could find. A native mud-and-wattle hut, built according to Gogo architecture, flat-roofed, with mud plastered on a framework of sticks tied together with bark. The manager, rejoicing in the name of Lazarus, had a *kanzu* with one sleeve, and the inevitable red fez on the back of his head; his assistant was a native with a nondescript cloth knotted over one shoulder and an ostrich feather stuck in his mud-plastered hair. Curry and rice eaten with the hands was twenty cents; tea with sugar and milk already added, served in a green enamel Japanese kettle and poured into handleless cups, was a similar price. We sat on rough-hewn wooden seats, and the table was a conglomeration of gasoline cases. Seeing the furniture, one itched in anticipation.

A quarter of an hour later I was again enthroned with my fellow-sufferers, an Indian lad who constantly tried to improve his English at my expense, and an Arab with a wealth of beard and a brick-red turban. He swore horribly as the truck bumped over the crazy road. Hearing that I was a doctor, he confided in me, giving full details of his internal make-up. He had the popular idea that his "bowels were plaiting themselves," or, alternately, that he was the proud possessor of a restless snake. He seemed disappointed when I advised him to obtain medical advice.

Four Africans, with all their worldly goods tied up in bright remnants of Bombay-produced cotton goods, tried to get shelter from the bitter east wind. I wrapped myself in a blanket and lay back, enjoying to the full the marvellous starlight and the phantom funnel of light through which we lurched and bumped.

The truck suddenly came to a halt. We were held up by an African sentry as we crossed the treacherous Ruha River. A fine bridge spans this fast-flowing, crocodile-infested river, and no unauthorized person might cross during wartime, since it was a vital link between the Union of South Africa and the northern battlefronts.

What a place! Only three months before a little girl came to draw water at this very spot. Her leg was gripped in the wicked jaws of a crocodile. She broke her pot over its foul snout and it let go, leaving the leg unspeakably mauled. All night long her parents kept her by the roadside, in the hope of getting a ride to bring her to the hospital. Early next morning she was jolted and bumped for forty miles in an empty truck to within twelve miles of us, and then her father carried her the rest of the way on his back. It had been a losing fight from the start, and the child had died as she was being prepared for surgery.

The sentry was satisfied with our permit, and, moving forward again, we suffered torture over the next ten miles. The road lay at the bottom of a steep hill, and the rains had eroded numbers of shallow, almost invisible ditches; we crashed into one after another of these, the whole truck shuddering. What that Arab said would have filled a volume. Arabic is very well suited, I believe, to situations of this sort.

At last the road smoothed out. Tall thornbush surrounded us. I was carefully calculating when we would arrive, since we were making a steady coverage, when the truck suddenly lurched to a standstill, and my calculations were forgotten. Not ten feet from me I saw the long neck and comical face of a large giraffe. Dazzled by our headlights, he didn't know what to do, so he just stood still, his ears twitching beside his apologies for horns. He stood for perhaps half a minute, looking at the truck, and then slowly turned around, twitched his tail, and giraffe-galloped into the thornbush, amid cheers even from the Arab.

Confronting us was a notice:

ESCARPMENT — 9 MILES
SLOWLY — *POLE POLE*
HATARI (DANGER)

Every twenty miles along the road are triangular concrete milestones. These are a monument not only to the efficiency, but to the methods of the Public Works Department. One day the milestones had disappeared. There were various theories — some said it was in memory of a plan to trap the Italians if they tried to invade Tanganyika — others thought they were to be replaced by larger and better milestones. A week later, however, the mystery was solved when a P.W.D. truck drove up and put back the stones, which had been taken to Dodoma for repainting.

These highlands are cold — sometimes you need two blankets at night. I felt a tremendous longing for those blankets. The rice bags seemed incredibly hard, the cushion seemed to have lost its ability to soothe, and I was more than relieved when the tall flour mill above Iringa township came into view. But troubles were still in store. A sleepy African stood firm by a barrier while myriad mosquitoes came to investigate. It appeared that trucks were prohibited from entering the town between sunset and sunrise. However, a compromise was arrived at after violent vituperation on both sides, and the vehicle was allowed to pass on its way to the hotel on condition that it returned to the barrier.

A sleepy night watchman showed me to my room, and I found a bed with a mattress that just enveloped me, and sheets and blankets that left my feet in full view when pulled up to cover my shoulders. I had made the necessary adjustments and was almost asleep when the night watchman entered without so much as a "*Hodi,*" and demanded *baksheesh,* a tip! I raised myself on one elbow and said some pointed things in his home tongue. "*Kah,* Bwana," said he in an awed voice, "I have sinned." He immediately made a tactful withdrawal.

There is something very soothing to the Australian in Iringa. The Germans, always keen on trees, had planted great avenues of eucalyptus. I sat under a giant blue gum, looking at the sky through the leaves and sniffing the scent of Australian bush. It is an unspeakable relief to get out of Africa for a little time occasionally, but this respite was only for a moment. A safari of ants had crawled up my leg and quickly brought me out of my daydreams of home. I made a dash for the hotel, feeling hostile to insects in general, and to ants in particular.

Half an hour later, insect-free, I went to visit my friend and patient, Jaffa Rhemtulla. He spoke eight Indian languages and two African. The only one we had in common was Swahili, and I was far from fluent in it. He gave me a cup of extremely weak tea, with a fly floating in it, and said:

"My heart is very full of thankfulness that once again I can see after years of blindness. Your little knife, and your medicines, have brought light to me, and the way your African dressers lived showed me that the message of Jesus Christ must be real."

"Yes," I replied, "Jesus, the living Son of God, has changed their lives, even as He has changed mine."

"What you did for me," replied the old Indian, "is much more than very much argument. Argument is merely words. But you and your African staff showed me Jesus Christ."

We talked for some time, and then, in a borrowed car, through twenty miles of slippery mud, I completed my journey, to find the reason for my urgent call had not been any vague and deadly tropical illness, but merely a plague of fleas!!

CHAPTER 18

Staff

GRANDMOTHERS are at the root of many troubles in Ugogo. These old hags mutilate the girls at their tribal initiation at puberty, practise all kinds of witchcraft and revolting tricks, and, by whisperings, rumor, and the use of the worst in native custom, do everything in their power to hinder progress.

Perhaps a girl wants to be trained in the hospital. She has had some education at our C.M.S. Girls' Boarding School, and is keen and shows promise. Her father is agreeable, but will not give his assent definitely. A week later he comes back with a long and plausible tale: she is needed at home to help in the garden and with the housework; her mother can no longer carry firewood. Behind the scenes there have been whispering and veiled threats.

Again it may be the father's fault entirely. He wants to increase his herd with his daughter's dowry, but he is quite indifferent as to whether or not she trains as a nurse.

To train African girls is no picnic. The actual nursing they like well enough, but the less agreeable side of hospital life does not appeal. We expect them to do consistently things that are contrary to their inclination and tribal custom. Often their response is passive resistance and the assurance that they will do it *bado* — later on. I soon realized what this meant, and spent quite a bit of time thinking of ways of countering this very African characteristic.

One morning Samson came to me in a great state:

"Bwana, you have given the junior nurses each a piece of peanut garden. They have planted their nuts, but have not taken out the weeds, and now their gardens look like jungle. I have spoken to them, but they laugh at me, so I wish to report them to you."

"I will tick 'em off, Samson."

"Thank you, Bwana."

I wasn't quite sure how to tick them off, so I asked the advice of the old Mugogo clergyman. He looked at me and smiled:

"Hospital girls are clean, well-trained, and well fed. They are very attractive to the eyes of the young men of the village, but when they marry, they must look after their gardens, and a good wife is a good gardener."

"Oh," I said, "and what do you suggest?"

"I will invite some of the young men to come to the hospital to look at the industry of the hospital girls, including their gardens. I will bring them tomorrow at ten o'clock. You inform the nurses at nine. That, Bwana, will cure the trouble."

"Thank you, Mika," I said. "Truly that is the wisdom of Solomon."

I walked up to the hospital, whistling a certain fragment from *The Mikado.*

Next morning, after staff prayers, I said:

"I have good news for you all. I have been impressed by the work done by the nurses" (a series of smirks greeted this), "and I feel that the young men of the village should get a true picture of the industry and the enthusiasm of my children in the hospital, so I have today invited the eligibles of the village to see your gardens."

Sechelela laughed outright. Utter dismay was on the faces of the junior nurses.

"*He-e-e-e-e,*" said one of them. "Who would have thought of his doing that?"

"*Kah!*" said another. "Truly he is *musugu* — the cunning one."

Daudi, in English, said to me:

"That sounds like the cunning of Pastor Mika."

"It is," I grinned.

Less than an hour later, a group of young men arrived. I met them at the gate and showed them the various sights, and finished up with a little oration in front of the overgrown gardens.

"These are the gardens of our nurses. This" — I indicated a spot with thistles three feet high on it — "is the garden of Elizabeti!"

Elizabeti stepped forward with her hands over her face.

"*He-e-e-e-e,*" said one young man, "her husband will beat her one day."

Elizabeti's one eye gleamed balefully between her fingers.

"This is the garden of Peristaci!"

It was a hopeless tangle of weeds. Her fiancé looked at it and spat. Rather pointedly, I felt.

That afternoon, a glum deputation waited upon me.

"Bwana, we want more hoes."

Next morning Samson came to me:

"I am wishing to report, Bwana, that the gardens of the nurses are in A-grade form!"

The marriage business is a very real problem standing in the way of girls coming to us for training. Early marriage is always advisable, the usual age being round about eighteen. If this comes about we have no trainees, and without trainees hospital work languishes, and all our aims for the future are frustrated. Many who start to train at the hospital are quite keen and enthusiastic for a time; then suddenly their work begins to deteriorate; they give trouble, and soon the news comes to us that a suitor has appeared.

Some married girls have combined home and hospital work, working on a part-time basis. This is not wholly successful and has the usual snags. Obstetrics do not run to schedule, and sometimes a wife returns late from the hospital, and the husband arrives home to find no dinner ready. There are mutterings, and often trouble.

These married girls are nearly all certified midwives, and it is a common thing to find a nurse, scrubbed up ready to conduct a confinement, with her baby on her back peering wide-eyed over her shoulder.

Much must be forgiven these girls when the heroism that often characterizes their work is seen.

The real foundations of our staff are the elderly widows, who are able to read after a fashion, but who cannot write. In their young days, no doubt, they were unspeakably trying to the pioneers, but now they have grown into the job. The same story will probably be told later on of the girls who now make us wish we were Job and Solomon rolled into one. We are building for the future, and can expect big things when the present generation are grandmothers.

I was talking over the whole problem of training unmarried girls with the head dresser.

"What will your young sister do when she leaves school, Daudi?" I asked tentatively.

He looked at me in surprise. "Why, come to the hospital, of course, Bwana. Are we not a hospital family?"

On the men's side, things are much easier. We have some quite well-educated lads who do their duties efficiently, and who become quite capable microscopists and dispensers.

One afternoon I walked out into our little pathology laboratory and found Daudi peering down a microscope, utterly intent upon his work. He was doing quite advanced blood work, and had a problem which he expressed in highly technical English:

"Bwana, what is this cell? Is it a myeloloblast, or a premyelocyte?"

We were soon arguing about it when above the window a grizzled head appeared, and without introduction, its owner requested me to buy a bundle of poisoned arrows. I examined them, and then turned to Daudi:

"Who is this old man?"

With a smile, the pathologist replied:

"My father, Bwana."

Incredulously I looked from one to the other. The father, a typical tribesman, with his dangling ear lobes, dirty loincloth, and cowhide sandals, and the son a skilful microscopist, speaking very fair English.

He is a sample of young educated Africa.

There are among the staff a few who speak English. Samson, the clerk, produces some wonderfully-worded reports, such as this:

> Sir: There is now no lice in the store; we wants five bags.

But Daudi holds the record with a request that I should buy him a pen with "a golden nib and no liver."

Judith, or Yuditi, as her name is in Gogo, speaks very correct English, and her welfare room is a great forward step. Daily she explains to mothers the why and wherefore of infant feeding, and modern methods have been modified to fit in with local conditions. Slogans have been translated into Chigogo and pictorial posters made to decorate the walls.

Mele mabi — bad milk — is a fallacy to be exploded. Mothers think that one breast produces milk that upsets the child. In reality, the coarse porridge, pushed down the baby's throat with the mother's thumb, is the cause; but since it is "our custom," it cannot be blamed. Yuditi explains the cause and the treatment as no European could, and shows the way to better things.

Modern health principles, necessarily, cannot directly apply in this country, where there are no clocks, and cows' milk is scarce. Cows there are in plenty, but they produce only a cupful of milk each. Also, they are milked by the thumb and finger method, and the dirty tricks that are often indulged in to give the milk a flavor are so revolting as not to bear repetition.

How to bathe a baby with a pint of water is a very necessary lesson to be taught in a place where water is so scarce; another is the washing of clothes with wood ashes by those who cannot afford two cents for a piece of soap. Other things are — avoiding skin diseases, making and using a cot, and the use of the "nappy" instead of their present system. In the native villages, father's one responsibility towards the child is to provide a dog, and if I tell you that its function in life is to be a peripatetic "nappy", I think your imagination will fill in the gaps.

It is slow, uphill work combating the tragic loss of child life, but with an African nurse teaching her fellows better methods and still retaining what is usable in native custom, great progress has been made. Getting among the staff, playing with them and working with them produces valuable results. The Sisters frequently play records for the girls and join in their very amusing games.

For my part, I played football, and was utterly outclassed by these nimble-footed youngsters. I could control neither the round ball, nor my irresistible desire to gather it and run.

However, I made my mark in Ugogo's national game, *Naga*. When the harvest is in, and the cornstalks have been eaten down by the cattle, the youths get ready for the fun. The dressers came to me *en masse* one Saturday, and said:

"Bwana, come and play *Naga*."

Nothing loath, I picked up my helmet and a heavy nobbed stick, and walked with them for five miles to a place midway between Mvumi and another village. On the way, the rules were explained:

Each man has his stick. The *Naga* is a small, hard nut the size of a golf ball, and the aim is to grab this and whack it in the direction of the opposition's village, follow on, and whack it again, until one or the other town is reached.

The losers then give a feast.

It is an extremely rough procedure. Sticks fly everywhere; broken limbs are common — but I have never once seen a man lose his temper, even after the most painful wallop.

I got in a few hits, and was cheered mightily. If anyone misses, both friend and foe jeer unmercifully.

At sun-down the game was adjourned till the following week. Sometimes it takes a whole season to finish a game, and hundreds of players turn out.

On the way home in the dark, we passed a huge baobab tree; fifteen men, with arms at full stretch, could just encircle it. A large hole in its side opened into a dark, hollow trunk. I threw in some lighted grass, and, in the wierd light, saw piles of human bones, white and old. Here, they told me, the victims of a long-ago smallpox epidemic had been stuffed, and now it was the haunt of leopards and hyenas.

The bones reminded me that I needed a set for my lectures. Once before, I had heard that in a famine year a number of unfortunates had crept into caves and died there, so I had gone to the place to collect some bones. When I produced these later in class, some of the students fled in terror, and I was told that it would be much better not to use them, or people would regard me as a witch of the worst character. I stored the bones in my garage, and they were a much better protection than any insurance policy.

The actual classes in treatment were very amusing. In the heat of the early afternoon I was walking up to the hospital with a bundle of books under my arm. I quickened my step as I heard an old Chevrolet flywheel being beaten with a piece of Ford axle. In two minutes my lesson would start, and it would never do to be late.

In the class sat the staff — fifteen uniformed nurses, five of them wearing veils, indicating that they had certificates and that they were trained Sisters. The other girls had heads shaven and rubbed with peanut oil. They were all barefoot, and as is the custom amongst the Wagogo women, they wore pounds of brass ornaments on their ankles. Opposite them were ten African lads in khaki shorts and shirts, and white aprons. Their hair was carefully parted, and they looked very spruce. It would be more accurate to say their hair was creased, because those tight curls could be made orderly only by the use of a safety-razor blade. The parting is cut in.

As I walked into the room, they all stood to their feet.

"*Misaa!*" I replied — "Good afternoon."

"*Mihanyenyi,* Bwana! — Good afternoon, Sir."

"*Yo yuli yunji mono yacereza?* — Is there anyone who was late?"

Three boys and two girls stood up, and, amid grins from their fellows, were seated on a special form.

On the table, in front of me, were three dressing trays, one containing eye-drops, and all the apparatus for treating eyes; another tray was for ear work; and a third one for dealing with gums and dental dressings. I took up the eye tray.

"Now, everybody, we are going to revise the treatment of eye disease. Sila, Kefa is your patient."

Kefa groaned.

"*Kah,*" said he, "and I was only a half a minute late. Is Sila not clumsy? Will he not put drops into my mouth instead of my eyes?"

"*Huh,*" grunted Samson, "you know what to do with your mouth!"

The class chuckled.

I wrote on a piece of paper, and handed it to Sila. He read it out:

"Lotion Zinc Sulph. and Golden eye ointment."

He poured some eye lotion into a bowl. A gasp from the class!

"Well," I said, "what did he do wrong?"

Elizabeti, the one-eyed nurse with a keen sense of humor, said: "Bwana, even with my one eye I could see that he did not pour away from the label, and behold, has he not messed it up?"

"*Kah!*" said Sila. He put swabs in the lotion, and proceeded liberally to bathe his patient's eyes. Boracic lotion poured down Kefa's face. He opened his mouth to protest. The lotion ran in. He shut it with a click.

"Well?" I said to the class.

"*He-e-e-e-e,*" said Othniel, a very junior dresser, "is he bathing him, Bwana, or just wiping his eye?"

Wide grins from the staff.

Sila took up the eye-dropper, charged it with blue eye-drops, and advanced in business-like style upon the unfortunate Kefa. None too gently, he pulled his eyelid up, and held the dropper grimly, with definite purpose.

"*Yah,*" said Daudi, "he thinks it is a crowbar!"

At least twenty drops shot into the patient's eye. He muttered rebelliously.

"Well," said I to the staff, "what of his treatment?"

"Bad, Bwana! Clumsy! *He-e-e-e-e,* he will drive people from the hospital."

Sila looked crestfallen.

"How shall we teach him?"

"Why," laughed Samson, "let Kefa treat his eyes."

"*E-e-e-e-e-e!*" said Kefa.

"*O-o-o-o-o-o!*" said Sila.

Now, Kefa was an expert. He picked up a soiled swab that Sila had dropped on the floor, and put it in the bucket. He asked for water to wash his hands, took the swabs from the bowl with forceps, wrung them out carefully, and swabbed the eye with a minimum of mess. Carefully, he put two drops into each eye, so that none was spilled, and finished up by putting a thin film of ointment over the eyelids. He stood back.

"Well?" I asked the staff.

"He has left his dropper on the table. It should be back in the bottle!" said one of the nurses.

"He has neglected to wash his hands after the work," said another.

"*Kah,*" said Sila, "and he has put the soiled swabs down my neck!"

One after another carried on with the demonstration. Bandaging was done; others measured out exactly the doses required by sick patients, and at four o'clock the musical note of the old flywheel ended the session.

Under the heading "Miscellaneous" in the wage book are the water carriers and the laundry-men.

Mhutila, the head water carrier, has one eye and two divergent buck teeth, and is quite a personality. When he has carried one hundred and twelve gallons of water (and in doing so covered some twenty-eight miles!) his day's work is over.

The laundry is presided over by a bow-legged ancient who stutters when he is not telling the truth — a most valuable trait from our point of view. In the same department is Dorika (Gogo for Dorcas), but unlike the lady of old, she is not full of good works. Her task is to wash the "nappies," and this she does by placing them all in a tub and jumping on them until she considers they have had enough. She also has a habit of throwing into the tall grass any that strike her as being particularly uncongenial, and then blaming the wind for their disappearance.

Once an owl flew into the surgery. I caught it. The Wagogo came to have a good look, but Dorika, after one glance, fled, her spindle shanks moving at an unbelievable rate. She is a Mukaguru, and they fear owls as the playthings of witches.

Of necessity, wages are adjusted to the cost of living, and leave little over. This applies to European and African alike. Several times some our our key African personnel have been offered much higher wages elsewhere, but have turned the offer down. It always seems to me that the sincerity of a man's faith is tested when his pocket is challenged.

CHAPTER 19

Train Travel

"WOULD YOU care for a lift, Doctor?"

An Austin Seven pulled up beside me, and the Sub-Assistant Surgeon at Dodoma Hospital held the door open for me. He was a Sikh, who had been trained at the Punjab Medical School. As we drove down to the post office together, I told him I expected to go on safari to Mwanza, and was hoping to travel on Saturday's train.

I had forgotten this incident until I went to book my seat on the train, when the tall, silk-turbaned station master, with a typical gesture of hands and head, informed me that:

"All is well, Doctor. I have heard of your going and have already appropriately booked."

My suitcases were crammed full, but still there remained a collection of articles which would not fit in. However, for a modest sum the local Indian tailor had made for me a large and capacious canvas bag. Into this went boots, rugs, mosquito net, dressing gown, the children's teddy bear, the *British Medical Journal,* in fact, everything not particularly breakable. These safari bags are grand things; there seems always to be room for just one thing more.

It was midnight as I finished roping it up. Everything was peaceful. The Southern Cross had gone over the horizon, but the Great Bear still twinkled in the night sky. I had gone to bed, and was just dozing off when the quietness was shattered by a loud *"Hodi!"* In the light of a smoky hurricane lantern, I saw outside my window a messenger, who had brought my instruments for eye surgery. His instructions had been to arrive early in the morning, and he had fulfilled them to the letter. It was exactly twelve-fifteen a.m.!

The train was half an hour late, and the local advocate, a Parsee, informed me that this was due to the "lamentable use of green wood as fuel for the locomotive."

I mounted guard over my luggage, and, in less than a quarter of an hour, saw people from all five continents, of seventeen different nationalities, and heard eleven different languages spoken. It was as good as a Cook's Tour, and considerably cheaper.

After much to-do and pushing here and there, the luggage was at last stowed away by the bearded Sikh conductor, who was adept at his job, and most helpful.

"Must apologize, sir, the train is too full," he explained, as he slid my suitcase under the seat. "I trust you will not be unduly inconvenienced by traveling first." My second-class ticket seemed very much out of place in the elegant compartment, fitted up with mirrors, a little cupboard for nick-knacks, a wash basin with a lid over it to serve as a table top, and two bunks affording sleeping accomodation. Eight shillings covered the supply of bedding and mosquito nets.

I settled down comfortably to make the best of my share of the two weary days during which the Tanganyika Express would pursue its leisurely way to the Lakes, traveling over plain and plateau that had many historical associations.

I was thinking of the days when this has been German East Africa when guttural accents and the lavish use of the hippo-hide whip had been the order of the day.

My musings were cut short by the African train-boy, dressed in a *kanzu* and an elaborate gold-braided waistcoat. Into the doorway of the compartment he poked his head, upon which was perched, at a rakish angle, the lace-work cap so popular with the Mohammedan Swahili:

"*Chakula tayari, Bwana* — Lunch is ready, sir," he announced.

As I stepped out of my compartment I met the Bishop of Central Tanganyika. We went to lunch together.

There is no effort or language difficulty in selecting courses, simply because there is no choice. The soup was one variety of the eternal chicken; the fish were caught in the lake; the mutton probably was goat, and the excellent coffee came from estates on the slopes of Kilimanjaro. Drinking coffee on the train is an art. The unwary who choose a table over the axle are nearly always humiliated, and try to look unconcerned when the hot fluid descends in a discomfiting deluge. A little goes a very long way!

My companion, the Bishop, was an amazing man. Once when, on the far side of Lake Victoria Nyanza, his car had broken down, he walked 150 miles through sleeping-sickness country to accomplish his purpose, the opening of a series of mission units on the very fringe of the Belgian Congo. As we chatted in the corridor, a tall African lad came from further down the train. Seeing him, the Bishop said:

"Oh, my dear Doctor, let me introduce you to a future member of your profession, from Makerere University in Uganda."

I shook hands with a most intelligent youngster, whose English was perfect. After a few conventional remarks, he said:

"My compartment is the last but one in this carriage, sir, should you care to come and have a talk with me."

I promised to have a chat later on in the day, and returned to my window seat to have a siesta.

The carriage window, apart from its everyday uses — for it has glass, a wood-slatted shutter, and an insect-proof screen — gives an ever-changing view of Africa. Tangled tropical growth, mountains, desert, plain, pasture land and lakes are all pictured in that frame. In the trip from the Coast to the Great Lakes you may see Africans from a score of tribes and in all stages of civilization. Some are in correct European dress; others in scanty cloths wound around them and knotted over their shoulders; still others in full native costume with ostrich feathers, black loincloth, bells on their ankles, mud in their hair, and a thousand and one different coiffures. There are hats of all sizes, shapes, types and ages.

The rainy season was just over, but already the grass was almost invisible; thornbush and baobabs were beginning to take on autumn tints, and the straggling remnants of what had been a wonderful display of convolvulus was all the vegetation to be seen.

From my window I caught sight of a sub-chief, wearing a red fez and blue coat over a khaki *kanzu,* riding along on a white donkey and attended by twenty followers, including his clerk and a native policeman.

Next I saw an old man seated on a rickety contraption built up in his garden. From here he pulled on a rope, to which were attached tins, bits of paper, and scraps of old clothing, to scare the birds away from his crop.

A little farther on I caught a glimpse of a young Gogo with a red beret-like collection of mud in his hair. He was taking pot shots with a bow and arrows at an abusive collection of monkeys that were raiding his maize.

Suddenly the country changed. The train slowed down and began to grunt its way up a stiff climb. We were going up the Rift Wall — a thousand-foot climb to the central highlands.

The country became a matted mass of stunted bush. The forest is full of all varieties of animal life — lion, leopard, rhino and elephant. Looking back, one could see the plain shimmering and white in the midday sun, a mirage giving it the appearance of a vast lake.

An appreciable increase in speed — we were approaching twenty m.p.h.! — showed that we had topped the first stage of the climb, and for the next twelve hours the train meandered along through country that had practically no variation. A junction at Manyoni provided the excuse for a twenty-minute wait. We got out and strolled along an avenue about four hundred yards long, which was lined with white and pink frangipanni.

Among the railway tracks, an Arab, finding it time for his afternoon devotions, laid down his load, unrolled his mat, and went through the full ritual of his prayers. The train started again, and he remained facing the East, reciting:

> "There is no God but Allah, and Mohammed is his prophet."

Every passenger had his own compartment, with his name inscribed on the card attached to the door.

Mr. Bhimji Ladha was a rotund, short-sighted Indian wearing his pink shirt over a most intriguing pair of baggy trousers that were bunched up about his ankles. A faint odor of curry emanated from his compartment, through the door of which I caught sight of a scene typical of an Indian merchant's kitchen at home. On the floor was a conglomeration of cooking pots mixed up with the children.

I was able to have a good view of all this, since the narrow passage was two-thirds blocked by the short-sighted Indian, who was engaged in an argument with his neighbor, a young beared and turbaned Sikh whose card indicated that he was one, Indur Singh. He seemed to be getting the worst of the argument, if a flood of Hindustani and frantic gesticulations were any criterion.

I managed to squeeze past them, with murmured apologies. Both parties immediately stopped their argument, and thanked me very much — for what, I had no idea, so I bowed and said "Thank you" in return.

My real object in making this hazardous journey down the corridor was to find the young African medical student and have a yarn with him. I stood for a moment outside his door, trying to decide whether an iced lime-juice was necessary. An iced drink is a luxury which almost justifies train travel in this country.

As I stood there in the corridor, I seemed to hear a new sound, and vaguely wondered what it was. In the train I had frequently heard Gujerati, Tamil, Hindustani and Sikh language spoken, as well as modern Greek, French, German and Swahili, but this had a sing-song timbre not common to any I had previously heard. The little card on the door furnished the answer: 'Mr. Chang Li Wong." The language was Mandarin. Most Chinese in Tanganyika are in the building trade, or else surreptitiously put gold caps on otherwise healthy Asiatic or African teeth whose owners have twenty-five shillings to spare.

Entering Charles Mtwali's door, I sat down with him to discuss his medical course. He showed me his Anatomy papers:

"Rather difficult in parts, sir, but the questions on the middle ear and radial nerve were directly from our lectures."

We discussed examiners and examinations at length. Then he told me how he had been educated at a Mission School and later at the Government Tabora School, where he had matriculated.

He said: "Of course, the maths. were only elementary. We spent more time on English and biology."

It seemed strange to be traveling so comfortably in a train over the country which, seventy years before, had been traversed so laboriously by Livingstone, and to discuss the angle at the base of an isosceles triangle with an African whose grandfather had once been a raw heathen.

He told me of cases he had seen in the five-hundred bed teaching hospital in Kampala, of humorous incidents in lectures and in the operating theatre. I closed my eyes and seemed to be back in the common-room of my medical school in the fourth year of my course.

He told me of his faith in God — how, when he was a lad at school, he had heard of Christmas and of Calvary, and of One who was the Son of God and had lived as a child in both Africa and Asia. He told me how he had simply enlisted under Christ's banner. We talked on for a while, and, quite naturally, the conversation turned to cricket, and I explained to him the difference between the googly and the leg-break.

I had dined and was considering going to bed when the Greek proprietor of the dining car put his head round the door:

"Doctor, would you care to listen to the B.B.C. news?"

"Thank you," I replied, and followed him down the swaying corridor. A minute or so later I sat in an easy chair and listened to the chimes of Big Ben, and heard the familiar voice of the announcer saying:

"This is London calling!"

I'm afraid I did not listen to the news. I looked out of the window and watched the tangled forest of the Great Central Plateau move slowly by, bathed in moonlight. Here I was, following the trail of that medical pioneer, David Livingstone. He had walked through that animal-infested jungle, his body fever-racked, his arm shockingly torn by the teeth of a man-eating lion. And here was I, seventy years later, sitting in comfort in an armchair, drinking iced water, and listening to the voice of a man speaking from London! Somehow, it did not seem to fit in.

When the hardy pioneer, by his indomitable will, had pushed through to Ujiji, on the shore of Lake Tanganyika, he was utterly cut off from the outside world. For five years he had had no word of his family, nor had he any news of world affairs. Stanley records how Livingstone reacted when he received his mail, letters that were two years old. He says:

> The Doctor took the bag, opened it, glanced at its contents, and read, with beaming face, one or two of his children's letters. Then he put the rest aside and asked for news of the world, saying he had waited so long for letters that he had been taught patience and could afford to wait a few hours longer.

Great events had occurred since Livingstone had been buried in the wilderness. The Suez Canal had been opened — the completion of the Pacific Railroad — the war between France and Prussia . . . .

With a jolt, the train stopped, within a few miles of Tabora, where the railway branches, one line going to Mwanza, on Lake Victoria Nyanza, and the other to Kigoma, on Lake Tanganyika. I stood on the carriage platform, and listened to the rhythmic beat of a drum somewhere over beyond the millet plantation that grew right up to the line. I could hear the clapping of hands and the beat of naked feet while the people danced, as they had danced when Livingstone had passed, three generations ago. There was the same matted thornbush, the same swarming insect life, carrying all manner of diseases. On the wind came the howl of the hyena, and the yelp of a jackal. It was Africa in its primitive state.

I watched the Kigoma train steam off over the plateau towards Lake Tanganyika. A few minutes later we proceeded slowly north through the night over the plains. The train boy came in to check up on the mosquito curtains and to spray the dark corners of the compartment with insect killer.

I crept into bed after briefly asking God to make me capable in some small way, of carrying on the work of the intrepid Scottish doctor.

There were the usual night noises, the bump, bump of the carriage wheels on the rails, the mixture of strange voices at each wayside station. I knew that there were one hundred and thirty-seven separate and distinct languages in the territory, but that night it seemed to me that the people at each station were vying with one another to use them all.

At one place I heard the roar of a lion in the distance, and my night's rest was broken into by wild dreams of the pioneer's difficulties in forcing his way through the jungle to open up the central part of the Dark Continent.

A few hours later I handed out my bags from the train on to the station at Mwanza, and gazed at the vast blue expanse of Lake Victoria Nyanza.

CHAPTER 20

The Lakes Safari

TO THE southwest of Lake Victoria is a stretch of rolling hills reaching out to Ruanda-Urundi and the Belgian Congo border. For the payment of ten cents — one penny — a mile, I was privileged to occupy the hard front seat of an Indian trader's truck, driven by a huge, muscular Nubian, who wore a multi-colored scarf round his head, a khaki shirt, and a pair of striped morning trousers. A most intriguing character, bullet-headed, with radiating scars on both cheeks, a smile that did full justice to excellent teeth and amazingly thick lips. This Chapanubi was *persona grata* with Arab shopkeepers, Indian merchants, and every Ali, Abdulla or Juma on the road. He greeted the District Commissioner as a personal friend, and bellowed his subordinates into a very un-African turn of speed.

On the western side of the Lake it rains from dawn till eleven a.m. The rain varies from a drizzle to a tropical deluge. We set out through the thick mist. The tall grass, weighed down by minute droplets, showered us as the truck skidded on its way. Occasionally a break in the fog showed the Lake, with the sun rising like a silver highway over a plain of lead, and with islands standing gaunt and black in the background. For miles the road was like a giant switchback. Hills that I would have descended in second gear were dealt with at unrecorded but breakneck speed. The speedometer had been disconnected; this, so the driver informed me, keeps down the tally of miles and increases the re-sale value of the vehicle.

Passing Rubungo, memorable for a mixed aroma of drying fish and coffee, we came to the densely-bushed, thickly-

Demonstrations, Wards, Clinics

BABY WELFARE

Open air demonstrations in Baby Welfare at the Jungle Hospitals are encouragingly effective in teaching the rules of common sanitation and baby hygiene.

"Our teaching had borne fruit. One woman delighted us with her clean, neat house. She showed us the baby's drinking vessel. Her flour, in clean wooden containers, was suspended in rope hangers from the rafters. There was none of the usual debris on the floor. Her kitchen had been built apart from the house. . . ." (Baby Week)

A Corner of Buigiri Hospital, North of Mvumi

Building the New Maternity Ward at Mvumi

Interior of the New Maternity Ward

Patients at an open-air clinic under a thorn tree at Kongwa

grassed country, uninhabited because of the tsetse fly. This nimble insect, resembling the March-fly, has a vicious bite, which may infect its victim with sleeping sickness. Miles upon miles of this type of country, and then, suddenly, banana groves again, conical-roofed huts, and signs of life. We climbed steeply, Chapanubi deftly double-declutching as we dropped from gear to gear until, on the top, he pointed to a far-distant collection of white buildings.

"That's Biharamulo, Bwana."

We had covered ninety-one miles in two and three-quarter hours, in a three-ton truck carrying a four-ton load. We drove up a wonderful grove of cassia to a German-built fort with walls three feet thick, and passed through a wide gate into the *Boma* courtyard. The District Commissioner's office was my goal. I walked in and introduced myself to the "Bwana Shauri," and received the immediate and welcome invitation to a cup of tea.

The *Boma* is the seat of Government activities, and is presided over by the District Commissioner, a senior in the Territory administration. Assistant District Officers are his subordinates, and help him to keep law and order and in making every effort to stimulate native advancement. As much authority as possible is placed in the hands of the chiefs, with the guiding hand of the Administration to curb or stimulate, as is required.

Each *Boma* has its Indian and African clerks, and typewriters click to the pounding fingers of spectacled Africans or turbaned Sikhs.

The *Boma* is huge and very German in character. Tradition has it that the three-feet-thick walls and huge arches were built with African blood. The rigors of the chain gang, starvation diet and *Hamsishirini* (twenty-five lashes with a hippo-hide whip) accounted for three hundred African lives in the building of this particular fort.

Standing on the wide verandas, you look through loopholes that were meant for defence, but give a wonderful view of the country from every approach. A flight of rough-hewn stone steps leads down to an old-world garden of roses, violets, forget-me-nots, lavender, and a crazy pathway covered with brilliant verbenas.

It turned out that we had to spend a night in Biharamulo. The District Commissioner was kindness itself, and gave us an unoccupied bungalow for the night. A touch of the unexpected came when he kindly offered to send hot water for baths.

"There is a particularly large porcelain bath," said he. There was — and in it a fine cobra! It was duly dispatched. You get used to scorpions in your boots, white ants that eat your boxes in the night, and the safaris of ants which walk into the house, and you, of necessity, walk out.

The first ninety miles had been easy. The next hundred were "B" grade roads, — that is, one shilling, seven and a half pence for its upkeep. I can vouch for its being second-grade. We were well on schedule, and it looked as if we would almost certainly arrive at our six thousand foot destination before sunset. However, we pulled up at Lusahanga, an imposing name for four grass huts at a crossroad, with a signpost indicating that Bukoba, the Lake port, was 135 miles away, and the Belgian border 86 miles.

For two solid hours we sat in the blazing sun while bags of salt were carried by indolent porters and carefully stacked in the truck; all luggage was taken off and then repacked. Then the driver had an altercation with an Arab, which evidently gave him an appetite, for, after that, he completely disappeared.

We ate bananas and studied our fellow passengers. On that truck, which was licensed to carry three tons and six passengers, were two tons of salt, huge bales of blankets, half a ton of merchandise, a forty-gallon drum of gasoline, six Arabs, an Abyssinian, and fourteen local Africans. At the very back were a pungent goat and a fat-tailed hairy sheep disputing the tailboard with an inverted bicycle.

At long last the driver appeared, and we were off once more. We had traveled half a mile when he became dissatisfied with a rear tire. We all got out while a pump was sought, and then it was discovered that the rubber tube was rotten.

We were in the middle of a swamp, where elephant grass and reeds ten feet high lined the roads. I pushed through these to a waterlily-covered pool, around which birds of the gayest plumage flitted; scores of bottle-shaped nests of yellow weaverbirds hung from the branches of a small tree whose leaves had all been stripped off by the tenants. A golden-crested crane strode sedately along, indifferent alike to the weaverbirds' chatter and to my presence.

A prolonged blast on the horn brought me back to the road, where I found that all was well again, apart from a series of concave springs and a new leak in the radiator.

For fifty miles we ground our way up a succession of steep hills and shot down equally steep descents. Between each lay a narrow, crazy wooden bridge that groaned and rattled as we crossed it, then up another five hundred foot slope in low gear. Every ten minutes the car was stopped for water. The "car boy," a sleepy local with a battered red fez and an equally battered double-breasted blue overcoat, unconcernedly took off the radiator cap and poured in muddy water from a rusty kerosene tin. He seemed indifferent to the shower of steam and boiling water that belched out of the damaged cooling system.

We had crossed one range, and now moved slowly over a grassy plateau, between small hills heavily timbered, except at their very tops, which were absolutely bald. It was delightful to see the hundreds of multi-colored butterflies flitting in their thousands about the road, over the swamps and under the humid tunnels made by tall trees whose branches met overhead. I mentioned this to the driver, and he laughed and said:

"There are *mbungo* here, too!"

I had never heard that word, but a red-hot pain in my forearm and a long, streamlined fly, with wings folded on its back, sitting on my shirt front, explained all. This is sleeping-sickness country. The beautiful butterflies were merely the sugar round the pill. For ten miles we swatted and dodged the bloodthirsty tsetse fly, each yell from the back of the lorry indicating a fresh victim. It was with relief that we passed again into a cleared belt and saw huts and banana plantations. Occasionally we stopped at picturesque villages of squat, round huts, with goats and chickens lazing round the doorsteps, native women carrying clay pots of water on their heads, and groups of little naked children, who came running to the car to shout a greeting.

On through rolling country; Durban's Valley of a Thousand Hills could not overshadow these rows and rows and tier upon tier of hills that faded away into blue mist over the Belgian border.

It became progressively colder as the sun sank, and when we pulled up before the Ruvuvu River at sunset, we dug coats out of the safari bag. The horn was blown, Chapanubi roared, and the deck passengers whistled shrilly, but no ferryman appeared till the sun had just set. Then he came, and said it was against regulations to carry cars after sunset; we must stay there all night. Mosquitoes came up in millions and the moon rose with the *shauri* in full swing, and only the threat of reporting him for not being on his beat at sunset, coupled with a musical jingle in my trouser pocket, worked the oracle. I kept quiet about the musical jingle — it was a can opener and a teaspoon. I had brought only a check-book and paper money with me, so he had to be content with a sense of duty done and a promise of *baksheesh* on the return journey.

The crossing was unique. The punt was an ordinary cable affair, but was pushed across the river by two tightrope-walking stalwarts. First the car, and then its load, were taken across. While the re-loading was going on, I strolled upstream in the bright moonlight. The trees reached right down and overhung the river; huge imprints in the mud showed where a hippopotamus had come ashore.

"Just here," said my guide, an African teacher, "is where a woman was taken by a crocodile when drawing water."

It was an eerie scene. The silent river, with its fast current, the dirge of the evening wind in the trees, the mystic twinkle of the fireflies, the distant throb of a native drum, and the cries of night birds. It was Central Africa untouched.

The moonlight was so brilliant that we drove for miles without headlights, through eucalyptus and black wattle groves lining the roads. Scenery lost its charm over the last stages of the journey, through hunger and the insistent feeling that one's bones were protruding and becoming permanently embedded in those unspeakable sisal cushions.

"Three miles to go!" said Chapanubi.

The words were hardly out of his mouth when the engine coughed and stopped. No gasoline! However, a tin of kerosene was duly poured into the tank, and, after a somewhat noisy interlude with the starter and choke we moved over the last stage of one of the most exhausting journeys I have ever undertaken.

Next morning I awoke in strange surroundings. The night had been spent in a circular grass-roofed hut. I was cold for the first time in Africa — really cold! I opened the door, and saw nothing but fog, thick, wet and clammy. I shivered, but cheered up under the effect of a cup of tea brought by a one-eyed lad, who enquired after my welfare in a strange tongue.

Slowly the mist rose, revealing rolling, green hills, stretching for a hundred and fifty miles to the great snow-capped peaks on the borders of Belgian territory and Uganda. In this outpost, two hundred miles from a doctor and a day's journey from the nearest post office, is the C.M.S. Bugufi Maternity Hospital. The lone Sister here is confronted continually with amazing problems.

She had a long list of people for me to see, and soon I realized that we would have a big day in the improvised operating room. Neither of the languages I knew was of any use, and everything had to be done with the aid of an interpreter. This is very irritating when you feel sure that the interpreter is adding little bits, and not quite getting your meaning across. In the afternoon I looked over my surgery list:

1—Removal of tumor, wrist. Local anesthetic. (Must allow relative to watch — of chief's household.)

2—Tumor of mouth. General anesthetic. Undoubtedly cancerous. Nasty anesthetic. Patient heavy drinker.

3—Necrosed jaw bone for scraping. (Little girl, very frightened.)

Then there were half a dozen minor things, such as teeth to be extracted, eye ulcers and abscesses. It was a full afternoon's work dealing with these. The next day I spent dispensing six months' supply of ointments, liniments and eye-drops, and going carefully into hospital statistics and finances.

I was determined to see something of Ruanda-Urundi, the upper portion of the Belgian Congo. The only available car was an old and very unreliable "Bedford." A number of enthusiastic youngsters pushed me down a steep hill, and, after a series of violent backfires, we spluttered our way along the main road to Ruanda.

This road led through tall grass and between banks covered with yellow daisies and masses of purple foxgloves. The slopes of the hills were like a huge mosaic with the varied greens of coffee gardens, banana plantations and acres of closely-planted beans. The road was cut from the sides of the hills, and had a sheer wall on one side and a hundred-foot drop on the other. Driving was rather interesting, since the old car skidded continuously in the red mud.

The tall grass, which overhung the car, showered us with seeds that pierced and irritated as we drove through. After thirty miles of this, we came at last to a papyrus swamp, with a rough bridge over a six-foot creek. An imposing black, yellow and red notice board indicated that we had entered Belgian territory.

We drove through a belt of gum trees, until a native, dressed entirely in a threadbare shirt and a pork-pie hat, held us up at a rough barrier and asked for our permit.

Not having one, and having little confidence in my French, I did not visit the Belgian District Officer.

We turned the aged vehicle and made the best of a journey home, which included pushing the wretched car up a steep hill and repairing a broken coil terminal with a safety pin and a lump of pitch filched from the battery.

CHAPTER 21

Baby Week

IT HAD BEEN a hectic week, the climax of months of preparation. In our spare time we had produced colored posters and thousands of typed pamphlets in the local dialect. It had been heavy work, but well worth the effort, for thousands of people from all over the country came to the hospital. Everything was new to them, and novelty is always attractive to the African.

Out-school teachers had traveled all over the five hundred square miles of our district, telling the people of the competitions and displays to be held at the Base Hospital. To a packed church on Sunday the African clergyman had preached from his pulpit on the necessity of healthy bodies and healthy souls. In characteristic African fashion he wove the Gospel story into the fabric of their everyday lives. It was a most impressive service.

Early next morning streams of people from the district made their way to the Assembly Hall of the Girls' School to see health plays. Five hundred men and women crowded in, while as many waited outside for a second showing. They watched, open-mouthed, as girls from their own tribe drew a skilful contrast between the medicine man and the medical man.

They depicted a native house with a sick child lying huddled in a corner. It was dark, and flies were everywhere, while every now and then a goat strolled over the stage. The witch doctor arrived, nodded wisely, made some incantations, and departed, dragging the goat by the hind leg as his fee. The audience roared with laughter. Then the witch doctor returned with a gourd half-filled with native medicine that he had brewed. The patient swallowed this and died. This scene was met with silence by the audience; it was all too real to them, and all too familiar.

The curtain rose a second time, to show a child being carried into the hospital, put in a clean bed, his case diagnosed and treated. The "doctor" (with my stethoscope, my white coat, and a very fair imitation of my voice and manner) ordered treatment, and, in an incredibly short time, the patient was up and ready to go home.

Everyone was greatly impressed by these little plays. To them it had not been acting, but fact.

The smaller girls of the school produced a skit showing the different ways in which mothers in all parts of the world carry their babies. Each child was dressed in the costume of the country she represented, and dolls, anointed with black boot-polish, were used as babies.

By the time the show had finished there were fifteen hundred people clamoring to get in, and the play went on without a stop all day.

Then there were demonstrations on the verandas of the wards. On long tables were illustrated the proper methods of weaning babies. Girls specially trained in mothercraft and child welfare from the C.M.S. Girls' School demonstrated the process recommended, which took six weeks, and during this period the child was gradually accustomed to gruel, from that of a thin, milky consistency to the thicker, more substantial variety.

All this was quite new to the native mothers, who gathered around the table, listening with astonishment.

One woman said:

"Why do you, who never have had a child, try to tell me, who have had ten, how they should be fed?"

"*Kah!*" replied the girl, "and how many of your children are still living?"

"I have two!" answered the woman, looking crestfallen.

"Well," said the schoolgirl, "if you had followed this wisdom you might have had them all now."

At another table we stressed the advantages of a varied diet, rather than living, month after month, on stiff, hard porridge with only one type of vegetable relish. Here again, the crowd, as they gathered round the table, heard something absolutely foreign to their ideas of diet. Some were intensely interested, but I frequently heard the remark: "But should we be able? Is it not forbidden?"

The Wagogo are very conservative in matters of food. Eggs are very abundant, but they never think of eating them. We showed them how valuable eggs are in preparing food for babies and invalids.

Farther on we had two miniature rooms, the first with a dirty floor and cooking utensils, flies, a mangy dog, and a sick child lying on the floor covered with a filthy black cloth. A poster was hung on the wall, explaining the dangers of dirt, and bearing the slogan:

"DIRT, FLIES, DISEASE, AND DEATH."

The other room was spotlessly clean, with polished cooking pots tidily put away. The floor had been swept and the drinking water had been boiled and was put in the corner, covered by a cloth, while the sleeping child was protected by a mosquito net, and was well and happy. The slogan on the wall read:

"NO DIRT, NO FLIES, NO DISEASE —
HEALTH AND LIFE."

There were huge crowds around this exhibit all day; it needed no demonstrator, for it spoke for itself.

Father, too, had his place in the exhibition. In the early morning there was a meeting for men only in the church. A pioneer missionary, who knew the Wagogo customs backwards, spoke very straightly to them. He said:

"In your herds, if the calves are sickly, what do you do?"

"We change the bull!" came back the reply in chorus.

"You do not blame the cow?"

"No, Bwana!"

"Then, why do you always blame your wives when your children die? Would it not be wiser to blame the husband?"

This was a line of argument that the men had never considered. They discussed the point at length, and we were able to drive home to them the need of dealing with venereal disease, showing them how it was the cause of many childless marriages and the huge infant mortality.

A competition had been arranged for fathercraft. Many ingenious cots had been made, and no two were the same. It was a condition that not more than twenty-five cents (three pence) should be spent in their making. They were constructed from bush timber and creepers that were available to every Mugogo.

To me, the most amusing of all was the cooking competition. Competitors brought their own cooking pots, fuel, flour and other necessities. It was a sight worth seeing to watch the crowd that gathered in the hospital kitchen, fully armed for the fray. The judges were the wife of the native clergyman and four educated African women. They went from exhibit to exhibit, tasting and spitting. The points most stressed in judging were the cleanliness of the cooking pots and the absence of lumps, the whiteness showing that the flour was clean, and its suitability for children. An interested and critical crowd watched the cooking and the judging.

Saturday was the great day. The Provincial Commissioner of the Central Provinces arrived, with other high Government officials, and was greeted by five important chiefs and a considerable number of retainers. A tour of the hospital was made, and everyone, both European and African, seemed truly impressed.

There were thirty mothers, with their babies, born that week, in the large maternity ward. The verandas were crowded with mothers carrying older babies, all of whom had been born in the hospital and had been brought for the great procession of children born in Mvumi Hospital during the previous few years. Five hundred took part in this, and each year group was preceded by a banner bearing the inscription: "FIRST YEAR," "SECOND YEAR," "THIRD YEAR," and so on.

It was amazing to note how the numbers had increased from year to year. The Provincial Commissioner confessed himself astounded to see in what large numbers the Wagogo women were coming to the hospital, and told me how little he had thought, a few years ago, that such a work as this could be done.

Then came the highlight of the whole campaign — the Baby Show. There were at least a thousand people round the place. Everybody seemed to be in the best of moods. The schoolchildren on the veranda of the hospital were singing their health songs over and over again. Behind the hospital, water was available for the bathing of babies that had been brought in for the competition. And what a squealing there was, when two hundred and thirty babies were brought in to be judged! I had to be the judge after all, since the high Government Official's wife, who was to have come, had malaria.

Daudi was at my elbow, and I tried to say something nice about every child that came along. This was not difficult for the first fifty or so, but when the hundred and twentieth baby arrived and I realized that we were only about half way, somehow my stand-in remark was wearing a bit thin. It seemed an excellent idea — as each child came along I looked at it and said:

"What a baby!"

This was sufficiently ambiguous to cover those who were strong and healthy, and the skinny little ones, who had few points that merited praise. It went down very well, but then I heard some of the mothers saying:

"What did he say about yours?" And the reply came: "He looked at my child, and smiled, and said: 'What a baby!' "

"*Yoh,*" said the second mother, "that is what he said about mine!"

The third one came up, and she said: *"Huh!* The Bwana knew a good baby when he saw one! He looked at my son, tickled his ribs, smiled at him, and said 'What a baby!' "

I looked at Daudi. There was a twinkle in his eye, and he said in English: "Perhaps, Bwana, you'd better change the medicine!"

So I mentioned specific points in each child. One little fellow was cross-eyed, and had obvious rickets, so I said: "How beautifully clean you keep him!"

Another child was completely healthy, and more than robust, but could hardly be classified as a violet. So I remarked feelingly: "How strong he is!"

Daudi developed a sudden cough! But by the time I had reached two hundred, I had come to the stage of merely making sympathetic noises as each child was demonstrated! Each and every competitor was given two pounds of rice, a piece of soap, and a small shirt for the baby. These had been made at home from men's socks that had reached the stage when they could be darned no longer. By some miracle of female ingenuity these seemingly worthless bits of footgear were turned into the neatest baby shirts, and were greatly prized.

I was priding myself on a difficult job done well when I heard two women discussing my impartiality. One said:

"Humph! What does he know about it, anyhow? He is only a man. What does he know of mothercraft?"

Another said: "Behold, he did not see the ulcer on my baby's neck, because I covered it with my hand."

And a third said: *"Kah!* Another child might get the prize, but mine is easily the best."

This started a violent argument, and I slipped away. I felt it was time to turn on the cow stew. It proved an excellent diversion. In no time grievances were forgotten, and vast quantities of rice, piled up high on trays, disappeared as convincingly as at a conjuring demonstration. The old clergyman came across to me.

"Bwana," said he, "may I speak to the people? A full stomach makes a contented man."

I nodded, and left him to tell his story in his own inimitable style. He pointed out how our hospitals saved lives. He had three children to demonstrate his points: The first had been given up as hopeless by the villagers some miles away, but hospital treatment had broken the power of cerebral malaria. Another child, who had faded away to a mere mass of skin and bone from dysentery, was hale and hearty. A third had been attacked by a hyena. His arm was in plaster, but he was well on the highroad to health. There were grunts of approval as he told their stories. And then the old man told how his life had been saved a week before.

"Behold," said he, "the medicines of the Bwana are a signpost to those who have eyes to see. They tell of the way to conquer pain and sadness. They are like the soup, that paves the way for the stew."

There was a murmur of approval at this.

"But remember," he continued, "the Bwana is only the signpost. He points you to his Master; to the Son of God, who came from His own country in heaven to help us."

And to a hushed audience he told the story of Calvary, of an empty tomb, and a living Christ. It was a dramatic and effective day.

I left the crowd watching a series of lantern pictures of hygiene methods, and slipped away for a cup of tea. On my way back to say farewell to the chiefs I was met by one of them who said:

"Bwana, if you will send a nurse to our town we will build the hospital. The children die like flies in our village, because our old women do not understand the things that we have seen today. We need this new way. We need a teacher to tell us the ways of God. And a hospital, to show us just how it works."

For weeks after, the primary topic of conversation in their homes was of the wonders of Baby Week.

A Baby Week campaign in the bush has its own particular interest, and is amazingly stimulating to the out-back people, many of whom have rarely seen a European.

We set out at dawn. It was a beautiful morning, and the track led through a forest along a narrow path hedged on either side by masses of flowers, and convolvulus climbing over every tree. As we approached the village a small boy ran out and blew on a bullock horn to announce our arrival, and almost immediately a large crowd gathered in a cleared space in the center of the village.

We started off with a poster talk. Mwendwa, the head nurse from Kongwa, had a large poster depicting the story of the progress of ten African infants. She hooked the posters on to a protruding beam of a native house and began her talk:

"Listen to what happened to these ten children!"

Brandishing a handful of cardboard babies, with rare skill she told the all too familiar story of death and suffering of Africa's child life. The reality of her demonstrations gripped her audience. One minute they rocked with laughter over some quip; the next they sat wide-eyed and open-mouthed as she explained the reasons of their babies' deaths.

Looking up suddenly, Mwendwa exclaimed, "Oh, I have finished them all off!"

"Well," said another nurse, "that is nothing new. The Wadala nearly always do that!"

Roars of laughter from the crowd showed their appreciation of this sally.

Next we taught them the health songs. These are cheery little ditties about insects, diseases, and how to deal with the various health problems. These songs either go to native tunes or to those of nursery rhymes. For instance:

Mazuguni, mazuguni,
Makali, makali,
Alenyi nye musugulwe

Malenga ga makandilo
Gakawa kulela muno muno
Mazuguni.

This is sung to the tune of "Three Blind Mice," and the translation reads:

Mosquitoes, mosquitoes,
They are dangerous, dangerous;
All of you be warned
That the water in the pits
Brings forth many
Mosquitoes.

Every house has these pits, which are the holes from which the soil is taken to plaster the houses. During the rainy season they fill up, and are used for watering the cattle. They are absolute death-traps, for mosquitoes breed in them by the million, spreading malaria throughout the village. It is the children who suffer most, for these bush people, who are steeped in superstition, find it hard to believe that mosquitoes cause fever when all their lives they have been taught that sickness is the result of witchcraft. To them a child with cerebral malaria has been bewitched, and therefore does not require medicine so much as a charm to keep him from the evil spirits.

For hours the people sang, and then we went to visit them in their houses. A year before we had shown them how to build better homes, how to keep them clean, the value of windows, and had urged them to build their cattle yards and kitchens away from their living quarters. Our teaching had borne fruit.

One woman delighted us with her clean, neat house. She showed us the baby's drinking water, boiled, and with his own special drinking vessel. Her flour, in clean wooden containers, was suspended in rope hangers from the rafters. There was none of the usual debris on the floor. Her kitchen had been built apart from the house.

"Why did you build your kitchen away from your home, Nyagula?" I asked.

Masai People

A GROUP OF
MASAI WOMEN
AND CHILDREN

"They are tall and slender, and go in for the most amazing bead and brasswork ornaments." (Kongwa-Berega)

A MASAI
AT ARUSHA

"In every way these fierce nomad tribesmen, who have wandered down from the Nile basin, are unlike the Bantu people of East Africa." (Kongwa-Berega)

High Award — and Forward

THE COVETED IMPERIAL BABY-WEEK SHIELD, WON BY THE KONGWA BABY WEEK

"Away in the animal-covered plains of Central Tanganyika hangs the highest honor the Empire offers in the Baby Welfare Sphere." (Baby Week)

DR. WELLESLEY HANNAH LOOKS FORWARD

(Handing Over)

"Oh, the smoke worried me," she replied, "and it made the place dirty."

Under the same roof were two small rooms occupied by newly-married young people, who seemed scarcely more than children. Their sole possessions were an ox-hide on the floor, a grain bin made from cow dung, and a hen sitting on some eggs.

Then we visited the little maternity clinic run by Lutu — Cigogo for "Ruth," a trainee of Kongwa Hospital. She told us that many women had been coming for prenatal treatment, and more and more were coming to her for confinement and advice on baby welfare.

In this campaign we traveled scores of miles. Each village had its talks, health songs and competitions. We could see the effects of previous campaigns in the increased numbers at the clinics, and in the improved housing and sanitation of these native villages, remote from civilization.

Incidentally, this Baby Week at Kongwa gained, among the maternity and welfare hospitals of the world, second place in the Empire Baby Week Competition. The next year was even more successful, for, on the sun-dried brick walls of this little hospital, away there in the animal-covered plains of Central Tanganyika, hangs the highest honor the Empire offers in the Baby Welfare sphere.

CHAPTER 22

Arusha and Kilimanjaro

WE WERE having a busman's holiday and planned to visit Arusha and Moshi. The town is in the shadow of Africa's greatest mountain. David and Rosemary were thrilled, Mary was full of preparations for safari. With a hurricane lantern to aid the light of the waning moon, I saw my crates and boxes carefully stowed away in the back of the truck. The staid Somali driver, in a startling blazer, supervized the roping down of the load, and, with the stars still shining in the early morning sky, we moved out of Dodoma, disturbing a host of sleepy crows as we moved through the native town on our way north.

The sun rose over the plain, and we settled down to a dusty hundred-mile drive to Kondoa Irangi.

An excited voice called from the back of the vehicle:

"*Ulanje,* Bwana, *zinhwiga!* — Look, Bwana, giraffe!"

Three splendid animals were gallopping, rocking-horse fashion, beside the car. They came right towards us. We could see their great necks and their curious, fly-swatter tails. They seemed to be coming right for us, but then turned off between some baobabs into the thornbush.

After miles of desert and dust, the Kondoa Lake was a welcome sight. As we passed, thousands of wild ducks flew into the air.

Kondoa town is an oasis, surrounded by erosion-scarred hills and wide, sandy river beds with the merest trickle of water in them. From the road the coconut palms and shady mango trees stand out deep green, and the white walls of the German-built houses made great masses of bougainvilleas more vividly purple.

We had left Ugogo and were in the country of the Warangi —a new tribe with a new language, new taboos and customs.

Scenes changed with startling rapidity. An hour before we shouted greetings to Wagogo, with their muddied hair and hugely-pierced ear lobes. Now our greetings were ignored; they were simply not understood by these folk with radiating scars on their cheeks and their shaven heads.

We climbed steeply, hairpin bend upon hairpin bend. At the top we stopped for one last look at that distant line of blue hills that had been our home for three years.

The driver slipped in the clutch, and we slowly climbed through heavily-timbered hills, the road deeply shaded by the leafy branches of giant trees. In the valleys were green patches of corn, with the deeper green of sugarcane in the swamps and beside the river.

Everywhere along the road were people carrying gourds, calabashes and tins. Women dashed to the side of the road, holding the jars on their heads; children stopped and shouted a greeting.

We stopped while the Somali driver supervised the filling of the radiator from a rusty kerosene tin.

I greeted a tall man who was carrying two gourds on a pole swung across his shoulder:

"Where are you going?" I asked in Swahili.

"To sell milk at the factory, Bwana," he replied.

Some of them had a walk of ten miles, but all were intent on getting a few cents from the creamery, where clarified butter was produced and later exported to Europe.

Rounding a blind corner, we nearly flattened a yellow-turbaned Somalilander, driving a herd of cattle north. His drovers fled pell-mell into the bush as our truck approached, leaving him to whack a path through the closely-packed mass of terrified animals. The driver let fly a string of Arabic, the on-top passengers yelled encouragement in Swahili, while a toothless Indian cursed the cows and their unfortunate owner forcibly in Gujerati — it was Babel let loose.

Suddenly the road fell away sharply. We had a glimpse of a fine lake, fringed with tall yellow thorn trees. In the background towered a cloud-capped mountain, and in the distance stretched a hundred miles of plain.

Beside the road small boys, stark naked, were herding cattle. They laughed and shouted and chased the truck.

One leaped directly in front of us. There was a sickly bump and a screech of brakes. I scrambled out, and saw his small body lying twitching beneath the front axle, his head only inches from the wheel. Fearing the worst, I reached out to feel his pulse. I had hardly touched him when he jumped up, and with a yell, sped off, absolutely unhurt. My cook, with great presence of mind, caught him, and taking him to a group of relatives standing spellbound by the roadside, produced a powerful impromptu speech on the dangers of the road, and the waywardness of children. We left amid profuse apologies — the victim the richer by a large, sticky lump of brown sugar.

A little farther on an imposing notice-board confronted us:

"PLEASE VISIT SHEER MOHAMED'S
FOR FRESH FISH, POST OFFICE, AND
THE CHEAPEST PRICES IN BABATI."

Six corrugated-iron shanties and a notice-board were all that Babati Town boasted.

Sheer Mohammed himself came out to welcome us. He took me to his *duka* and offered me a seat, moving untidy piles of gaudy cloth and sweeping a bag of onions from a chair. Then he removed a tin of kerosene from the one he was to occupy himself. He poured me out a cup of sweetened, weak tea, and gave me effusive thanks for the free advice that he should come to the hospital for an ophthalmic operation. I paid my shilling, and put my ten "fresh" fish well out of range in the back of the truck.

Standing beside a beehive-like hut was an imposing African armed with a butterfly net. His task was to stop all southbound vehicles and search them for tsetse fly. He solemnly saluted us with his net.

We moved on through heavily-timbered country, the air alive with brilliantly-colored butterflies and myriad other insects.

A recent storm had turned a patch of black soil into a glue-like morass, and wheel marks showed where a large truck had gone through. The driver desperately rushed the mud patch trying to avoid the huge ruts. The machine plunged forward, slewed, recovered, skidded again, and then, with a sigh, the engine stalled. We were down to our axles in the slimy, glutinous stuff. We got out to view the position, and decided to try to drive out by a series of side skids. Swarms of tsetse flies descended upon us. They bit fiercely right through khaki drill. It was a hectic quarter mile of pushing and chocking, dodging and swatting. At last we got out from the bog, crab-fashion.

The plain stretched before us, the towering Rift Wall on our left, with a large shimmering lake at its foot. We drove through miles of native-planted cotton, and surprised a herd of zebra feeding beside the road. They scampered off amongst the tall grass. Game was everywhere. Gazelle, large and small, stood looking at the truck as it passed within a few feet of them. Farther out in the plain a dozen wildebeeste and a lesser koodu grazed. Three ostriches chose to cross the road as we passed, and ran beside us for nearly a mile, with long, smooth strides, at thirty-five miles per hour. They dashed down a hill and into a thicket, disturbing a group of eight giraffe, which looked up mildly and at once resumed daintily choosing the greenest leaves from the tops of great umbrella-like thorn trees.

In the excitement of watching animal and bird life, we had not noticed that the clouds had lifted. Majestically the fourteen thousand foot crater of Meru stood out sharply in the setting sun, and behind it, some hundred miles away, the snow-capped peak of Kilimanjaro. These two giants towered above the plain, with its radiating chains of hills. The reds and golds of the sunset were reflected in pale rose-pink on the distant snows of Africa's greatest mountain.

Our arrival in Arusha was an anticlimax. We developed tire trouble, and limped through the coffee plantations and banana groves that line the last few miles, into the most congenial town in Tanganyika.

Next morning, leaving my wife to haggle with a Singalese merchant selling fine materials at small prices, I explored the town. I strolled under the shade of huge trees into the main shopping center. Two mountain streams, reputed to contain trout, flank the town. Where the main streets converge is a clock, each face telling a different story. Just beyond is a most up-to-date hotel, claiming to be:

ON THE MID-POINT OF THE CAPE TO CAIRO ROAD
BUILT AT THE VERY CENTER OF AFRICA

Meru towers above the town, its foothills a mosaic of greens. Higher up are bamboo forests, where rhinoceros and elephant abound; while at the edge of the crater, in vast gullies, are thousands of tons of volcanic ash. I was told that a much better idea of the mountain could be obtained by driving along a road going up the lower slopes. I decided to try it.

At first we drove easily up a wide, grassy road between native shops. Then it became steeper and narrower, till it was nothing but a footpath, and I had no choice but to turn the car. I backed cautiously, and went just too far. The edge of the bank crumbled under my rear wheels, and the car jerked backwards into a thickly-packed mass of nettles and creepers that grew on the almost sheer face of a forty-foot waterfall. I climbed carefully out of the car, which was lying at a perilous angle, and examined the tangle of undergrowth. I felt sure it would not support the old bus for long. With difficulty, I got out the stout rope that is essential to a car's emergency equipment on African roads, and, having placed large stones behind the front wheels, anchored the front axle to a tree with the rope. My brief stay in the nettle bed had been incredibly painful, and I felt that the position generally was not of the best.

Things looked up a bit when the local chief arrived. He was dressed well and the proud wearer of a set of ill-fitting false teeth. Inquiring if he could be of any assistance, he called some fifty scantily-clad, ochre-stained warriors of the Warusha tribe and directed operations till we were pulled and pushed to safety.

I presented him with a five-shilling note, with which he promised to buy two legs of beef to regale our deliverers. He raised his helmet, and we waved farewell to the cheering braves as we drove down the steep slope en route for Moshi.

A game reserve, the Sanya Plain, lies between Arusha and Moshi, and the game make the most of it. Two immense giraffe blocked the road, a herd of nearly two hundred zebra grazed quietly in the tall grass. There were literally thousands of Thompson's and Grant's gazelles.

On both sides of the road stalked numbers of ostriches. The bones of wildebeeste gave evidence of a lion's recent kill, and two jackals were making the most of what the hyenas had left. As we rattled on over the corrugated volcano ash road, Meru, with its crater, lay behind, while on our left Kilimanjaro towered, cloud-covered.

Leaving the plain, the road wound through a jungle of creepers and cactus. We crossed a dangerous brick bridge over a gorge, where a pitched battle had been fought in the 1914-18 struggle.

Seeing a notice, "TO MACHAME," I decided to renew the acquaintance of a white-haired American doctor, and to visit his hospital on the southern slopes of Kibo. The narrow road was for miles an ever-ascending avenue of tall cassia, shading both road and acres of shining-leafed, white-flowering coffee, everything a vivid green. The furrows carry snow water from the mountain slopes. The banana groves, the lawn-like road, the tall gums, made the very light seem green. Directly above, through a break in the clouds, glistening white, were the snows of Kilimanjaro. As the sun set, Kibo cleared of cloud; she seemed to have a pale-pink spotlight playing upon her; the shadows crept up and up till only the top portion of the glacier was tinted, and soon a majestic study in black and white stood out against the night sky.

Many have climbed the nineteen thousand foot peak, and several have lost their lives in the blizzards that sweep the glacier, but none has a mountaineering record to equal that of the amazing little man I met that evening. He had been trained in a Caucasian military school, and had fought in Persia, in the World War, and against the Red Russians. In this latter fight he had left his pulpit to command his town's defences. He had turned back an armored train with the threat of a mined bridge, and with an ammunitionless machine gun! He spoke fluently twenty-four European and Asiatic languages, and five African dialects. At one time he had been a Professor of Hebrew at a Scandinavian University, and he is a world authority on Arabic language and custom.

Now an educational missionary, he traveled from school to school supervising and instructing. His car had broken down, so he shared my safari. We bought supplies in the crowded Indian quarter of Moshi, visited the station which serves both Kenya and Tanganyika railways, and, with due ceremony, obtained a gasoline permit.

Moshi, above all, is a hot and dusty spot, and we thankfully made our way to the spacious veranda of the general store, where the locals meet to gossip and drink tea. Dr. Roesch and I sat sipping ours when a member of the Mountaineers' Club joined our party. He was an Alsatian, and wanted to know whether I was a Doctor of Divinity. Hearing that I was merely a medical missionary, he told us a story about a padre who had once visited Moshi in the days when services were held in the courthouse.

Nearly all the European population had turned out. The preacher was vividly describing Belshazzar's feast. With a dramatic gesture of his hand above his head, he said: "They looked. And, behold! Writing in a foreign tongue upon the wall!" All Moshi followed his hand, and there, sure enough, was writing, but this time it needed no interpreter. In Swahili, in huge letters, was written:

"USITEME MATE — DON'T SPIT."

The talk turned to mountain climbing. I was surprised to hear that Mawenze, the minor peak of Kilimanjaro, was far and away more difficult to climb than Kibo, with her glaciers and crater.

Our French friend insisted that we should share what he termed a bachelor's lunch. His home was on the slopes of Old Mochi, opposite a derelict rubber plantation.

Soup, fish, roast beef, pancakes and maple sugar were set before us, and then, to cap it off, a huge dish of bacon and eggs, our host remarking: "But is it not the national dish of the British?"

We moved on to Marangu on the eastern slopes of Kilimanjaro. Half-way up the steep, winding road, cut from the hillside, the car spluttered and stopped. I tinkered with the carburetor, but the only way we could get up was to drive backwards up this narrow pass. The mountain was on one side, and a five hundred foot drop on the other. I chose to keep near to the hillside, but, in turning a sharp bend, a rear wheel went into the ditch. My heart sank. I got out the jack, but it would not go under the axle. I tried chocking timber under the wheel, but made no headway.

"Could I not lift the wheel again back upon the road?" asked the doctor.

I looked at his five feet four-inches, and smiled.

"She weighs thirty hundred pounds," I said, and regarded that as THAT.

Dr. Roesch, however, said: "You will permit me to try, perhaps?"

Imagine my feelings when this amazing little man not only lifted the wheel out of the ditch, but pushed the car back on to the road! Later that day, I saw him bend a copper cent piece in two with his bare hands, and swing enormous two hundred pound dumbbells about. When no one was looking, I had a try with those dumbbells and nearly burst a blood vessel lifting them knee-high.

Over coffee, he told me of his experiences in various parts of the world. He produced a "Black Jack," a lethal-looking weapon of plaited leather loaded with lead. A brisk crack on the back of the skull, he informed me, was uniformly successful in fracturing the skull and yet leaving no bruise. It was a present from a Chicago policeman. It appeared that three thugs had attacked this limb of the law and were "kicking him in the slat," when the small Doctor of Divinity applied a little ju-jitsu and "turned the table upon them."

A nine-chambered Mauser revolver in his collar box drew out the story of a journey on foot disguised as a green-turbaned Dervish on a pilgrimage to Mecca. He traveled through Mombasa, the Somalilands and Arabia, and saw what few "Unbelievers" have ever witnessed — the frenzied dance of the Dervish and the ritual of their secret societies.

Only the use of the revolver, an amazing knowledge of Arabic, a bottle of Cognac brandy, and the recitation of chapters from the Koran saved him from a frantically hostile crowd on one occasion.

He had climbed the summit of Kibo, the major peak of Kilimanjaro, forty times. He waved aside this unparalleled achievement, and said:

"But it is so easy with the sardine and the prune for the diet!"

I shall always associate this humble little man, with all his achievements, with the great of Africa. Somehow my last picture of him, standing on the slopes of the mountain he had so often conquered, reminds me of what I have always imagined David Livingstone to be.

On one safari I stayed a week with this little Caucasian linguist. From his house a wonderful panorama unfolded itself.

At the foot of the mountain was Moshi. Beyond it were range upon range of hills — the Pare Mountains, where

General Smuts so convincingly defeated the East African German force in the 1914-18 conflict.

I had climbed a hill from which there was a view extending far over the Kenya border. On my way home I came upon a splendid avenue of young fir. I stopped before a stone house set in the middle of an extensive coffee plantation. As I stood admiring the splendid crop, a young African, dressed in khaki, came to the door. I addressed him in Swahili. He took my outstretched hand, and said:

"If you would prefer, sir, to speak in English, I am quite conversant with that language."

He was a chief of the Wachagga, a most progressive and powerful tribe, living on the slopes of Kilimanjaro. He invited me into his house, and I sat in an armchair, upholstered with leopard skin. It was a tastefully arranged room. I was most impressed by the way in which it was decorated. On one wall was a picture of Tabora College, where the Government trains chiefs' sons and the future leaders of the country. On his mantelpiece were cups that he had won for athletics. On one of the walls were various football and cricket groups. Without a doubt, I was looking at Africa as it will be in a generation or two. It was a very peaceful place, and I was enjoying the quietness when a most unusual noise behind me made me nearly jump out of the chair. Petro, the young chief, laughed, as I looked round, rather self-consciously, to see a cuckoo clock!

He took me into his office. There was his typewriter, which he used expertly! But the thing that attracted my attention was a Bible — a well-worn one, beside his blotting pad. Seeing me look at this, he smiled:

"I keep it there, Doctor, because I use it regularly. You use your medical books frequently, and keep them on hand, and you're constantly referring to your road map when you're on safari. My Bible means all that, and more, to me."

"In what way, Petro?"

"It was years ago that Dr. Roesch was here — the little man with the strength of an elephant."

"I know it! He lifted the whole car when I bogged one wheel on a mountain pass on the way up here before."

The African smiled: "Have you seen him lift two hundred pound dumbbells?"

I nodded.

"Well, Doctor, it was through those dumbbells that I came to know Jesus Christ. He taught me ju-jitsu, and then told me how Jesus was a man's Savior, that it was no easy path that He asked you to follow with Him. The Doctor told me how he gave his life — lock, stock and barrel — to Jesus. So I started reading the Book, and there could be only one result! I asked Jesus to come into my life as my Savior, and my Counsellor. It's not very easy to be a chief among these people. But it's a different story when you work in harness with the Son of Almighty God."

I nodded. "That's exactly my experience, too, Petro."

CHAPTER 23

Handing Over

IN THE Government Service in Tanganyika Territory a man works for thirty months and then has eight months' leave. I had done forty-two months, the last six of which had been the most testing of my life. My old enemy, asthma, was becoming rampant, and leave had to be considered.

Then I heard that a relief doctor was on the water and would shortly arrive in Dar es Salaam. I had vivid recollections of my own arrival there, struggling with the Customs in an inferno-like corrugated-iron shed, followed by a night in an unspeakable hotel, and not being able to speak a word to the swarms of Africans who, I knew, were most anxious to take me down. Generally speaking, my first contacts with Dar es Salaam were a nightmare memory.

I remember feeling that I was a most insignificant stranger in an extremely strange land. Then I started off my career there with a most frightful *faux pas,* which did not exactly herald an auspicious beginning to my work. This is what happened:

During a visit to the laboratory where the famous Robert Koch had done some of his epoch-making pathology, I was looking at a dilapidated photograph of the great man when I felt a touch on my shoulder. I turned to find the Medical Registrar standing beside me.

"You know, old man," said he, "you ought to sign your name in the Governor's book. It's the 'done thing'!"

I thanked him, and straightway went to fulfil my duty. I walked along roads where frangipanni, flamboyants, bougainvilleas and crotons of every shade made an amazing color effect. Government House stood out white amongst its green lawns and tall palms. I passed through a gate where a huge, blue-fezzed African soldier of the King's African Rifles presented arms with a flourish. I was a little non-plussed by this, and somewhat at a loss to know how I should acknowledge it, and gave a very half-hearted salute in reply, after which I proceeded to write my name in the Governor's book.

Back at the hotel again, I found my wife was sick. Whether it was the water or the heat, I have no idea, but before midnight we all lay groaning in misery, perspiring and sleepless, listening to the swish of the fan and the buzzing of countless mosquitoes.

The next day we were still prostrate. At intervals I struggled out to buy bottles of ginger ale, as we felt we could not face Dar es Salaam's water supply. In the early afternoon an African messenger arrived with a very imposing blue-crested envelope. Opening it, I read:

> His Excellency the Governor requests the pleasure of the company of Dr. and Mrs. P. H. H. White at a Sundowner.

I was completely at a loss. I did not know what a "Sundowner" was in Africa. In Australia, a Sundowner is a swagman, a man seeking work, but that did not fit at all. I groaned. The type of acute illness from which we were suffering was a positive bar to any social activity. Furthermore, I was completely in the dark as to the technique of reply, and had no one to advise me. This was when I dropped my brick. I replied, according to the usual formula, "regretting," but GAVE NO REASON!

I had disobeyed a Royal Command and didn't know it!

Next day the family's pains began to disappear, and my wife was so much better that she went out and bought a hat.

I visited the hospital, and found a friend in the surgeon. In the course of conversation, I blandly told of my invitation to Government House and of my reply. I knew the worst when I saw his shocked face. He dashed for the telephone and rang a very high official, and I confessed all.

"Never mind," said the official, "forget about it. I'll fix it up for you."

I did forget about it — but, unfortunately, so did he!

I had vowed that I would never let anyone suffer as I had on arrival at Dar es Salaam. So, when I heard of the expected arrival of Dr. Hannah, I traveled to the coast to meet him.

Along the waterfront there is an avenue of crimson flamboyants, and, as I waited for the ship to come in, I strolled along past whitewashed Government buildings and the palms that grew near the beach. I was thinking of my first meeting with Wellesley Hannah. I can still see him, a fragile-looking lad, finishing the mile only a few feet behind the winner in a time five seconds better than any clocked in fifty years of Australian Inter-Varsity athletics. I thought of how our friendship had grown, and how he was coming now to take over the job which I had started.

Soon his ship steamed in through the bottleneck of the harbor, passed the wreck of the German dry dock (a grim relic of 1914) and anchored in midstream. Immediately a horde of small craft were rowed out to her loaded with dealers in silks, ebony elephants, and brassware. Indians and Africans crowded round the landing stage. At last I saw my friend being rowed ashore. I forced my way through a collection of African porters bearing down on what they regarded as their legitimate prey, and grabbed hold of Hannah, piloting him through the motley crowd and into the town, where we talked at length over a cup of tea.

Dar es Salaam to me is always a depressing place. The slightest exertion leaves one in a bath of perspiration. We sweltered in the hot afternoon sun. We sampled the joys of swimming in the tepid water at Oyster Bay, walking delicately on sharp coral. In the evening we explored the Indian Quarter together, its shops, crowded tenements and mosques, and purchased mosquito boots, hurricane lamps and quinine (from the post office!), and then saw his luggage safely loaded on the freight train.

The next day we successfully paid our official visits, making no *faux pas* this time! It was with infinite relief that we settled ourselves in the train and started our journey up country, leaving behind us the town, with its noisy crowds and cosmopolitan life.

Slowly the train made its way through the coconut groves and rice fields of the coastal flats and gently climbed the Pugu Hills. A mass of green tropical growth, trees closely packed together and entwined with vines, completely covered the slopes.

In the middle of this jungle the train drew into a station. Variously dressed Africans ran beside the track, shouting to their friends in the crowded third-class, while vendors cried out their wares to the passengers — oranges, pineapples, and coconuts. We were thirsty, but we hesitated to drink from the filter on the train, since we had seen the train boy fill it from a very ordinary watering can. However, a five-cent piece changed hands, and, with a deft cut of his knife, the grinning salesman presented us with a coconut brimful of first-rate thirst quencher.

"What is the idea of making the line curve so violently?" asked Hannah, looking at the engine, which seemed to be running parallel to us at that moment.

"Well, the explanation, as I have heard it, is that the Germans gave the contract of this line to a Greek firm, who were paid by the mile for the railroad laid," I replied.

"Someone must have made a jolly nice profit!" smiled my friend as the train went over on to the other track.

As we meandered through the hills, I pointed out the melancholy sight of acres of rubber trees struggling to keep above the undergrowth.

"Some enterprising Teuton put his savings into planting that little lot in the German East Africa days, but he picked the wrong variety, and went broke!"

Beyond the coastal ranges lie mile upon mile of sisal, reaching out in orderly rows as far as the eye can see. Tanganyika leads the world in sisal production. The long, pointed leaves grow like an immense pineapple top, while the central shoot resembles a gigantic stick of asparagus.

As dusk fell we carefully lowered the mosquito wire over the windows. In the darkness the train climbed up and up until peering through the mosquito net at midnight, we saw the name "MOROGORO." We had climbed the Uluguru Mountains and reached the edge of the Central Plateau.

A fiendish row goes on at night. The plop, plop, of logs of wood being loaded into the tender, the worried shouting of the Asiatic guard, and the babel of strange tongues as Africans wander up and down the platforms at each station. As a background to it all, there comes the buzzing of insects and perhaps the roar of a lion.

After a restless night, we awakened to find ourselves in the Central Plains. Guinea-fowl scuttled away into the bush; baobabs, almost leafless now, stood out against the sunrise; Africans, wrapped in blankets, drove their cattle to pasture. As we gazed through the window together, I pointed out to Hannah various phases of Gogo life that came into view.

There had been a washout on the railway line, and we were held up for hours. To fill in the time, I taught my successor some Chigogo greetings. Later in the afternoon we finished our journey in a 1924 Ford. Over the final stage we had rather an exciting race, arriving in Mvumi just ahead of a torrential rainstorm.

Handing over was a hectic business. Together we pored over records, statistics and accounts, checked up drug lists, and ploughed through bulging files of office correspondence, as I tried to initiate him into the vagaries of hospital life in Africa.

After weeks of hard work, the day came at last for me to set out for Dodoma on the first stage of my journey back to Australia. I was saying good-bye to the African staff and to all the people who had come to bid me farewell, when the African clergyman — my friend and counsellor in a hundred and one difficult situations — drew me aside and said:

"Do not worry for the hospital, Bwana. Dr. Hannah is *muswanu* — a good man. The Wagogo like him, and will come to him."

That evening we stood looking over the plains of Ugogo. I was leaving before sunrise the next day. Neither of us felt much like conversation. We stopped under a thorn tree and bowed our heads, committing ourselves and the whole work to God; then grasped hands and parted.

I knew the job would go forward.

Glossary

Glossary

Sw. — Kiswahili.	Ch. — Chigogo.
Askari (Sw.)	A soldier.
Bati (Sw.)	Corrugated iron.
Bibi (Sw.)	Lit. "Grandmother." Actually up country it is used as a term of respect to women; in the towns it is sometimes a term of disrespect.
Boma (Sw.)	A fort, or palisade.
Bwana (Sw.)	Sir.
Chigogo	The language spoken in the Central Plains, Ugogo.
Debe (Sw.)	A kerosene tin.
Dhobi (Sw.)	A laundryman.
Dudu (Sw.)	An insect.
Duka (Sw.)	A shop.
Fundi (Sw.)	An expert, or tradesman.
Funza (Sw.)	A ground flea.
Godown	A storage shed.
Heya (Ch.)	Yes.
Hodi (Sw.)	May I come in? (Equivalent to knocking).
Ipu (Ch.)—Mapu (pl.)	Abscess.
Jambo (Sw.)	Good-day.
Kabisa (Sw.)	Absolutely.
Kah! (Ch.)	Exclamation of surprise.
Kanzu (Sw.)	A night-shirt-like garment.
Karibu (Sw.)	Come in.
Kaya (Ch.)	A Gogo house.
Kiboko (Sw.)	A hippo-hide whip.
Kiswahili	The common jargon of Tanganyika, Kenya and Zanzibar.
Kumbe! (Ch.)	Behold!
Mbukwa (Ch.)	Good-day.
Mhungo (Ch.)	Malaria, or merely a fever.
Mudala (Ch.)—Wadala (pl.)	An old woman—also native midwife.
Muganga (Ch.)—Waganga (pl.)	Witch doctor, or medicine man.
Mugogo (Ch.)—Wagogo (pl.)	A tribesman of the Central Province of Tanganyika.
Mukombi (Ch.)-Wakombi (pl.)	An old man.
Mutemi (Ch.)	The Chief, or King.
Muzungu (Ch.)-Wazungu (pl.)	A European.
Ndio (Sw.)	Yes.
Shauri (Sw.)	A court case, or a discussion.
Safari (Sw.)	A journey.
Sikukuu (Sw.)	A party
Shenzi (Sw.)	Heathen or uncouth.
Ugogo	The Central Plains of Tanganyika.
Vipece (Ch.)	Cataracts—opaque eye lenses.
Wacho! (Ch.)	Rot! I don't believe a word of it.
Yaya gwe (Ch.)	Oh, my mother!
Yobwa (Ch.)	Ibis.

The Jungle Doctor Series
by Dr. Paul White

JUNGLE DOCTOR
JUNGLE DOCTOR ON SAFARI
JUNGLE DOCTOR OPERATES
JUNGLE DOCTOR ATTACKS WITCHCRAFT
JUNGLE DOCTOR'S ENEMIES
JUNGLE DOCTOR MEETS A LION
JUNGLE DOCTOR TO THE RESCUE
JUNGLE DOCTOR'S CASE BOOK
JUNGLE DOCTOR AND THE WHIRLWIND
EYES ON JUNGLE DOCTOR
JUNGLE DOCTOR LOOKS FOR TROUBLE
JUNGLE DOCTOR GOES WEST

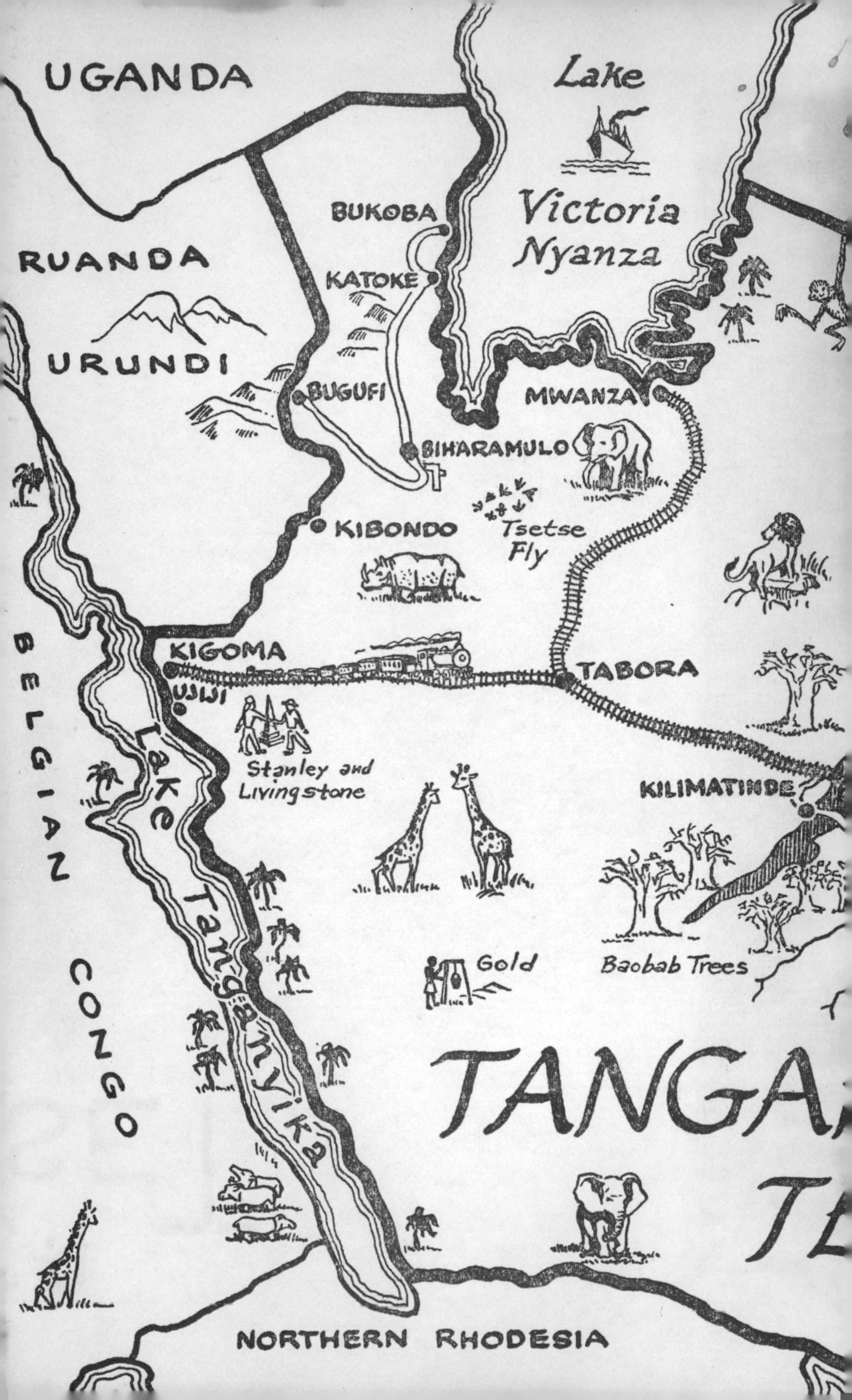
UGANDA
Lake
Victoria
Nyanza
BUKOBA
RUANDA
KATOKE
URUNDI
BUGUFI
MWANZA
BIHARAMULO
Tsetse
Fly
KIBONDO
BELGIAN
CONGO
KIGOMA
TABORA
UJIJI
Lake
Tanganyika
Stanley and
Livingstone
KILIMATINDE
Gold
Baobab Trees
TANGA
TE
NORTHERN RHODESIA